CW00689499

The Princess A Nun!

A NOVEL WITHOUT FICTION

ALSO BY HUGH ROSS WILLIAMSON

History and Biography

LORENZO THE MAGNIFICENT

CATHERINE DE' MEDICI

HISTORICAL ENIGMAS

CHRISTOPHER MARLOWE ('KIND KIT')

WILLIAM SHAKESPEARE (THE DAY SHAKESPEARE DIED)

SIR WALTER RALEIGH

KING JAMES I

GEORGE VILLIERS, FIRST DUKE OF BUCKINGHAM

THE GUNPOWDER PLOT

FOUR STUART PORTRAITS (Lancelot Andrewes, Gerbier, Eliot, Rainsborough)

JOHN HAMPDEN

CHARLES AND CROMWELL

THE DAY THEY KILLED THE KING

JEREMY TAYLOR

Historical Novels

THE PASSING OF THE PLANTAGENETS

A Chronicle of the hundred years from 1459 to 1558 comprising 1 The Butt of Malmsey (1459-1478) 2 The Marriage made in Blood (1478-1522) 3 A Matter of Martyrdom (1522-1541) 4 The Cardinal in Exile (1541-1553) 5 The Cardinal in England (1553-1558)

THE QUEEN-MOTHER OF FRANCE

comprising

1 The Florentine Woman (1558-1572) 2 The Last of the Valois (1572-1584) 3 Paris is worth a Mass (1584-1593)

CAPTAIN THOMAS SCHOFIELD (1644-1647)

THE SILVER BOWL (1661)

JAMES BY THE GRACE OF GOD (1688)

Historical Plays

HEART OF BRUCE

ROSE AND GLOVE

HIS EMINENCE OF ENGLAND

QUEEN ELIZABETH

TERESA OF AVILA

GUNPOWDER, TREASON AND PLOT

Historical Places

CANTERBURY CATHEDRAL

THE ANCIENT CAPITAL (WINCHESTER)

THE FLOWERING HAWTHORN (GLASTONBURY)

HUGH ROSS WILLIAMSON

The Princess A Nun!

A NOVEL WITHOUT FICTION

LONDON
MICHAEL JOSEPH

First published in Great Britain by Michael Joseph Ltd
52 Bedford Square, London WC1B 3EF

1978

ISBN 0 7181 1457 4

Filmset in Great Britain by
D.P. Media Limited, Hitchin, Herts.
Printed and bound by Redwood Burn Limited,
Trowbridge and Esher

Contents

'The Princess a nun! That will be the end of this House!'

The Prioress of Pastrana, on hearing that the Princess of Eboli had become a Carmelite.

Author's Note

Illness has restricted my movements during the writing of *The Princess A Nun!* and I am indebted to Julian Rathbone for much research and editorial help in the final stages. Julian is a fine novelist in his own right and his contemporary and historical knowledge of Spain was invaluable.

HRW

To Sarah and Nigel
in
memory of their grandmother,
Elizabeth Sprigge

I
Ana Acquires a Convent

Ana de Mendoza y la Cerda, Duchess of Pastrana, Princess of Eboli, had from childhood been accustomed to have her least whim gratified. The habit persisted into her years of maturity and, as she had been married at thirteen to Ruy Gómez, the King's intimate friend and the most powerful man in Spain, there was very little she could not have for the asking. One of the rare refusals was indelibly memorialised. When she was fourteen one of her pages had refused to do her bidding and in the physical fracas that ensued – politely termed a duel – she lost her right eye. The black silk patch, diamond-shaped, which she wore to cover the loss had, with the passing of time, acquired the character of an honourable decoration and the courtiers vied with one another in their compliments on the beauty of her left eye. Though she had 'only one sun', they said, that single orb was sufficient to illumine the court of King Philip of Spain – and the world beyond it. She herself was, according to a madrigal written by Antonio Pérez, one of her husband's secretaries, 'a precious stone set in the enamel of nature and fortune'. The King himself, however, though the gossips credited him with being her lover (on no firmer evidence than that the eldest of her ten children was fair and bore a slight resemblance to him) was less complimentary. 'She wants everything that comes into her head,' he said, 'and sticks at nothing to gain her end; her rages and ill-words are unparalleled for one of her rank.'

The latest thing that had come into her head was to found and endow a convent for nuns vowed to poverty. Her plan materialised when, on 28 June 1569, the little house she had provided a stone's throw from the ducal mansion in Pastrana was consecrated, in the presence of a select number of courtiers from Madrid, forty miles away, and an immense crowd of villagers and local peasants who sang the responses to the litanies and danced rhythmically in the dust. The Mother-Foundress of the Carmelites who observed rigidly the Primitive rule of the Order was the 54-year-old Teresa of Avila and she, in her white mantle and black veil, was the last in the procession to enter the new chapel convent which was the fifth of her famous 'foundations' made in the two years since she had received permission to return to the original Carmelite rule of absolute poverty.

Ana had first met Mother Teresa seven years earlier when they were both staying in the Toledo palace of Ana's aunt, Doña Luisa de la Cerda, the widow of the Marshal of Castile. The widowing accounted for the nun's presence there. When her husband died, leaving her one of the three richest women in Spain, Doña Luisa, devout Christian though she was, was inconsolable and time, far from healing her grief, intensified it to a pitch at which her family and friends feared for her reason. At length the youngest of her attendants persuaded her to 'send for the saint at Avila' – for such already was Teresa's reputation among the discerning – and, under obedience though with considerable reluctance, Teresa came.

'It disturbed me a little and distressed me a great deal to think that she wanted me to come to her because she believed there was some good in me,' Teresa recorded, 'but the Lord was pleased that the lady should be so much comforted that she began at once to be markedly better and felt more comforted every day. She conceived a great affection for me, as I also did for her when I saw how good she was. She was a most God-fearing lady and so good that her most Christian spirit made up for what was lacking in me.'

For Teresa, however, it was a penitential exercise to have to live among such luxury and splendour and she came to realise that Doña Luisa had her own environmental stresses. 'I saw that she was a woman and as subject to passions and weaknesses as I was myself. I learned, too, how little regard ought to be paid to rank and how, the higher the rank, the greater are the cares and the trials that it brings with it. And I saw that people of rank have to be so careful to behave according to their position that they are hardly allowed time to live. Even their meals have to be regulated according to their status rather than their stomachs. I hate the very idea of being a great lady. God deliver me from all that sinful fuss!'

It was Teresa in this mood whom the Princess of Eboli met when she came to stay with her aunt, Doña Luisa. Almost immediately they were at odds. Ana, having found an additional channel of influence in the friendship of Philip's young Queen, the beautiful Elizabeth of Valois, explained this to the nun and asked her to name what favours she would like her to procure.

'Princess,' said Teresa politely, 'I thank Your Highness, but a daughter of God needs nothing but God.'

Quite apart from the nature of the reply, Ana disliked the use of her title of Princess. As a wedding gift to Ruy Gómez, King Philip had presented him with the Principality of Eboli in the Kingdom of Naples. To Ana, intensely proud of her great Spanish heritage (Spain had no princes outside the Royal House), this was a doubtful compliment. She persuaded the King to raise the property of Pastrana to a Dukedom and then persuaded her husband to get rid of his *parvenu* Princedom and alienate his Eboli estates. It was as Duchess of Pastrana that she preferred to be known and accepted 'Princess of Eboli' as the conventional address of the uncomprehending bourgeoisie. In her aunt's house it bordered on an insult.

Teresa, however, was only too happy to accept Doña Luisa's help in making the first of her Foundations of traditional Carmelite convents. Doña Luisa also gave her a house and provided an adequate endowment for a convent at Malagón and María de Mendoza, sister of the Bishop of Avila – Ana's cousins – made a similar gift for one at Valladolid.

Thus eventually it became a matter of prestige for Ana not to be outdone by her relatives and on Whitsunday 1568, Teresa, who was putting the finishing touches to her foundation in Toledo, was visited by a servant from Pastrana, with a carriage to take her to Ana. Teresa explained that circumstances made it impossible for her to go to Pastrana at the moment.

The servant replied that this would be awkward, because his mistress was already there and had gone solely to discuss the provision of a convent; and that if he returned without the Mother-Foundress his mistress would be most offended.

'Nevertheless,' Teresa confessed in her autobiography, 'I had not the slightest intention of going, so I told him to stay and have a meal, and said I would write to the Duchess before he left. I then went into the presence of the Most Holy Sacrament to beg the Lord to show me in what terms to write so as not to cause the Duchess annoyance, for from every standpoint it would be well to have Ruy Gómez on our side, as he has such influence with the King and everyone else.' Teresa then, as was her invariable custom, consulted her confessor, with the result that she set out next day for Pastrana where Ana and Ruy Gómez, her husband, impatiently awaited her. On the way, she met a hermit who was also going to Pastrana because Ruy Gómez had given him 'a good hermitage and a place where a group of hermits could settle', and he promised her that he would make this over to her new Order and himself take the Carmelite habit.

'The Prince and Princess of Eboli gave me a very warm welcome,' she admitted. 'They allotted us a lodging to ourselves, for the house for the convent was so small that the Princess had had a large part of it pulled down and rebuilt; its outer walls had not been demolished but a great many alterations had been made inside. I must have been there three months, during which there were many trials to be borne, as the Princess wished to do certain things which were not fitting in our Order and I determined that, rather than do them, I would leave without making the foundation. Ruy Gómez, with the commonsense he has to a very marked degree, saw reason and persuaded his wife to modify her demands. I, too, gave way in certain respects.'

Ana wished to nominate a nun of a different Order as a member of the new convent. On this point Teresa remained adamant in refusal. She would have no nuns already trained in the observance of another and different Rule. On financial matters, however, she was prepared to compromise though she found it exhausting when Ana haggled over the amount of revenue she had offered the day before and the next day quibbled over the regularity of the allowance, finding endless points for discussion and trying to turn them into points of dispute. Had it not been for the help and understanding of Ruy Gómez who, over the years, had learnt the art of controlling his wife without quarrelling with her, Pastrana would have had neither convent nor friary. For the latter, he paid an engineer a considerable sum to bring water to the top of the hill where the hermitages were grouped. He did it secretly 'so that the village should not cease giving the friars alms', regarding it as a mere ducal responsibility. Also to avoid any unnecessary argument with Ana.

Ruy Gómez de Silva, a Portuguese who had been King Philip's friend from their boyhood together, was now the ablest of his ministers. When Philip's father, the Emperor Charles V, decided that for dynastic reasons his heir should marry Mary Tudor, Queen of England, he sent Philip to England with the great Duke of Alba, twenty years the young Prince's senior, as one of his advisers, and Ruy Gómez as the other. In this way the Emperor hoped that the two different generations and outlooks would each make its contribution of wisdom. Also, as there was hardly a single topic on which Alba and Gómez did not violently disagree, it ensured that every matter would be extensively discussed. This was the old Emperor's technique for ruling his far-flung dominions which included Germany, the Netherlands, Spain and the Americas – to use two ministers who hated each other in order to discover more about any matter than both together might have told him had they been friends.

Philip continued the practice, and was careful that only himself knew to which he was inclined until he announced his decision. He remained on excellent terms with both but with the difference that, as was acutely defined, 'the Duke of Alba was the friend of the King, but Ruy Gómez was the friend of Philip'.

Before their departure for England, Ruy received two marks of royal favour – a dukedom and marriage with thirteen-year-old Ana de Mendoza y la Cerda*, one of the greatest names and fortunes in Spain, whose great-grandfather, Pedro González de Mendoza, Cardinal Archbishop of Toledo, had been known as 'the third King of Spain', at a time when the other two were Ferdinand and Isabella. From him, Ana had inherited the restless vitality, the unscrupulousness and the arrogance which made many courtiers wonder whether Ruy's marriage to her had really been the benefit that the old Emperor had intended; but at least Ana's personality and her fortune gave to her husband's party at court a more-than-adequate counter-balance to the formidable Duchess of Alba in the rival group.

* As was often the case where minors were concerned, the marriage was not consummated nor the household established until she was eighteen.

Ana's insistence on Mother Teresa's convent at Pastrana was not unconnected with her wish to obtain what had so unaccountably become a fashionable honour before the Duchess of Alba could do so; at the time she had greatly approved of Teresa's remark to that Duchess, when she was shown a room crammed with Alba treasures worth several king's ransoms: 'What good can this heap of objects be?' Yet even in her most perceptive moments, Ana had no understanding of the reason which drove Teresa to desert the comforts of the aristocratic convent in which she had spent twenty-five pleasurably undemanding years to found a new Order committed to absolute poverty with houses all over Spain where, to remedy the ravages of heresy, the Blessed Sacrament should be reserved, and adored.

Teresa had had a vision of hell.

'It was the Lord's will', she wrote, 'that I should see the place which the devils had prepared for me there and which I had deserved for my sins. This happened in the briefest space of time, but even were I to live for many years, it would be impossible for me to forget it. The entrance, I thought, resembled a very long narrow passage, like a furnace, very low, dark and closely confined; the ground seemed to be full of water which looked like filthy, evil-smelling mud and in it were many wicked-looking reptiles. At the end, there was a hollow place, scooped out of a wall, like a cupboard and it was here that I found myself in close confinement. But the sight of all this was pleasant compared with what I felt there. This is no exaggeration. Indeed my feelings, I think, could not possibly be exaggerated. I felt a fire within my soul, the nature of which I am utterly incapable of describing. My bodily sufferings were so intolerable that, though in my life I have endured the severest sufferings (the worst it is possible to endure, the doctors say, such as the shrinking of my nerves during my paralysis), none of them is of the smallest account by comparison with what I felt then. And even these are nothing by comparison with the agony of my soul, an oppression, a suffocation and an affliction so deeply felt and accompanied by such hopeless and distressing misery that I cannot find words to describe it.

'In that pestilential spot, where I was quite powerless to hope for comfort, it was impossible to sit or lie for there was no room to do so. The very walls, so terrible to the sight, bore down upon me, but I realised that it was a great favour that I should see with my own eyes the place from which God's mercy had delivered me. It is nothing to read a description of it, or to think of different kinds of torture (as I have sometimes done, though rarely, as my soul made little progress by the road of fear) for none of these is anything by comparison. I was terrified by all this and still am as I write of it. Since that time everything has seemed light to me by comparison with a single moment of such suffering as I had to bear during that vision.

'That vision, too, was the cause of the very deep distress I experience because of the great number of souls who are bringing damnation upon themselves, especially the Lutherans. The harm and havoc being wrought by these heretics troubled me very much and as if I could do anything in the matter, I wept before the Lord and entreated Him to remedy this great evil. I felt that I would have laid down my life to save a single soul that was being lost on their account. It breaks my heart to see so many souls travelling to perdition.'

It was to give what help she could that Teresa, though she 'particularly disliked journeys, especially long ones', set about to make her foundations to ensure that the Lord would be praised in each house and that the Most Holy Sacrament would be reserved there. 'It is a special consolation to see one church more when I remember how many the Lutherans have destroyed. I cannot think of any trials, however severe, that we need dread if we can bring such a blessing to Christendom.' The smallness and poverty of her foundations were of no account as long as they could safely house the Blessed Sacrament.

In proclaiming this emphasis, Teresa had gone straight to the heart of the matter. The religious wars and persecutions which were making Europe a shambles were centred here. Teresa, in common with all Catholics, believed that when, in the sacrament of Holy Communion, the priest pronounced over the bread and the wine Christ's words at the Last Supper: 'This is My Body: this is My Blood', the bread and wine became the Body and the Blood. The heretics held that they remained bread and wine.

Had the matter been a mere philosophic exercise, it would have been of little consequence, but as both parties believed that this was the core of the Christian religion and that Holy Communion was a necessity for life after death (in accordance with Christ's words: 'Except ye eat the flesh of the Son of Man and drink His blood, ye have no life in you: whoso eateth My flesh and drinketh My blood hath eternal life and I will raise him up at the last day'), there was, literally, nothing in life of equal importance. And belief expressed itself in action. King Philip's subjects in the Netherlands were increasingly embracing Protestantism and, two years before Ana had sent for Teresa, they had given spectacular evidence of it in Antwerp itself.

On the feast of the Assumption of Our Lady, 15 August 1566, a mob surged into the cathedral and took the famous mediaeval image of the Virgin Mary which had been placed on a side altar after being carried in procession and, helped by a company of prostitutes, rolled it in the mud. The crucifix over the High Altar – one of the masterpieces of mediaeval art which was the pride not only of Antwerp but of all Flanders – was hacked to pieces. And the Blessed Sacrament was taken from the pyx in which it was reserved and solemnly fed to a parrot. The rioters then proceeded to deal in a similar way with the other churches of the city and their example was followed throughout the country until about four hundred churches had been gutted.

King Philip when he received the news was for once unable to mask his feelings. 'It shall cost them dear,' he said, 'I swear it on the soul of my father.' He sent Alba, with a force of 20,000, to restore order and set up a Court of Inquiry in Brussels.

The King's own devotion to the Catholic Faith was intense. In 1563 he had laid the foundation stone of a new palace at the foot of a protecting cliff of the Guadarrama range about thirty miles to the north-west of Madrid (which two years earlier he had chosen as the capital of Spain instead of Valladolid). The action was the fulfilment of a vow he had made when his troops were victorious in a battle fought on St. Lawrence's Day 1557, and the new palace was to be built in the form of the gridiron on which the saint was martyred. Moreover, El Escorial was to contain, as well as a palace, a monastery with its church, a mausoleum for the monarch of Spain and a library. The long line of cloisters with their intervening courts served for the bars of the gridiron; the four towers at each corner of the monastery represented its inverted legs; and the slender length of the palace furnished the handle. The great granite building* was to take twenty-one years to complete, but from the very first days of its construction the King was a constant visitor, staying at the outset in the house of the parish priest and hearing Mass from a private stall which consisted of a three-legged stool screened by such an old and tattered cloth that he was easily visible through the holes in it. On one occasion, it was said, he came in late and, sitting on a bench by the door so as not to cause a disturbance, was mistaken by a visitor for one of the building workmen.

When at last his own rooms were ready in the Escorial, his study looked out on the wide, barren Castilian landscape

* 'Still,' as Sacheverell Sitwell says, 'the eighth wonder of the world.'

and the dark alcove which served as his bedroom adjoined the monastery church, with a small connecting door opening on the High Altar, so that he could follow Mass from his bed when he was too ill to get up. To some of his attendants, it almost seemed that the huge edifice had been erected to protect this cell, with its view of the altar, so that the King might have the consolation of knowing that the Blessed Sacrament was guarded by strong walls and that he had seen to it, to the best of his ability, that 'in Spain at least the sacred light burned on in tranquillity'.

The heretical outbreak in the Netherlands, however, by entangling religion with secular ambition and international politics had given rise to problems which involved moral issues of terrifying complexity. And, as King, he had a responsibility which no one else but his confessor could share. This he must explain to a certain Mother Teresa who had met his sister in Toledo at Doña Luisa's palace and by her had sent him a message: 'Blessed is the soul to whom the Lord gives an understanding of His truth. To increase faith in believers and to enlighten heretics, a wise king would willingly lose a thousand kingdoms, for to gain a kingdom of which there shall be no end is the more advantageous thing. Remember, Sire, that Saul, though anointed, was rejected.'

When Philip received Teresa's letter, he realised at once that it answered the questions with which he had been wrestling in his prayers, and he said to his sister: 'Where is this woman? Can I not see her?' But Teresa had already left Toledo for Pastrana and the King had to postpone actually meeting his uncalled-for adviser, though he unequivocally endorsed the advice. He wrote to his ambassador at the Vatican, charging him to communicate it privately to the Pope: 'I would lose all my realms and give my own life a hundred times over rather than suffer the least schism in religion or in the service of God. I have no intention of reigning over heretics. I shall try to smooth out the religious difficulties in the Low Countries without recourse to arms, if it is still possible, for I see clearly that a war would involve the country in total devastation; but if matters cannot be put right without armed intervention, I am resolved to take up arms and take part in the battle myself.'

As soon as the Pastrana house was dedicated, Ruy Gómez and his two principal secretaries, Antonio Pérez and Juan de Escovedo, set out for the Escorial, whither the King had summoned them for an urgent conference on affairs in the Netherlands. But Teresa went back to Toledo, travelling uncomfortably in the oldest and shabbiest cart that Ana could find. Her request for it was prompted by an unfortunate incident. A visiting priest had seen her getting out of the ducal carriage outside the door of the convent and had shouted at her: 'So you're the saint who is deceiving everybody, preaching poverty and riding about in luxury!' Teresa thanked him for being 'the only one courageous enough to point out my faults', and decided to avoid carriages for the future.

Ana showed every sign of sympathy and understanding as together they selected a wretched farm cart, but privately she decided that it would make an amusing story with which to regale Court circles in Madrid to which she was returning to boast of the new convent which had been entirely designed, financed and equipped by herself.

II
The Problems of King Philip II

The road from Pastrana to El Escorial lay through Alcalá and Madrid, and Ruy Gómez's original intention was to leave Escovedo in the university city to make a report on recent student disturbances there and Peréz in the capital to collect and evaluate the latest gossip of the various Court factions. But on consideration the Duke decided it would be wiser to keep them both with him in case the matters the King wished to discuss were of such complexity that their immediate advice would be useful. Besides, as he was training them to enter Philip's service when the time came – soon, he hoped – for him to retire from it to find peace in the simplicities of country life at Pastrana, it was as well that they should have as much first-hand knowledge as possible.

Ruy's relationship with the two secretaries mirrored, in a sense, the pattern of the King's relationship with Alba and himself. Antonio Pérez and Juan de Escovedo could be relied on to voice antithetical views of any situation and to take opposite sides in any argument. Ruy would listen patiently and form his own opinion. In their attitudes to him, it would not be unfair to say that Escovedo cared for him as a man and Pérez as a statesman and Ruy responded to the difference by often secretly respecting Escovedo's advice even when he publicly endorsed Pérez's.

There was no doubt that in the ways of the world and in diplomatic acumen Pérez had the greater skill. He was the bastard of Gonzalo Pérez who was for many years a secretary of state to both the Emperor Charles V and Philip. When he was five he was legitimated by a diploma of the Emperor; by the time he was in his early teens he was precociously *au fait* with the ways of the Court, and his father, realising that Prince Philip's inseparable friend held the key to advancement, got him taken into Ruy Gómez's service. He was now thirty-two, delicate in health, thin, over-perfumed and, according to an Italian visitor at Court, 'tenacious of being thought much of and of people offering him presents'. Escovedo, on the other hand, was almost obsessed with integrity, incapable of the least action which might be interpreted as 'accommodation'; deeply but not ostentatiously religious and, at twenty-eight, still touched with a boyish priggishness. His wife, being asked on one occasion by Pérez's wife why the Escovedos were so much poorer than the Pérezes, said truly 'Because we have kept our hands clean.'

The matter on which the King wished now to consult Ruy Gómez was one requiring the advice of a friend rather than discussion with a minister. It concerned the doings of the 21-year-old General of the Sea – that is to say, Commander-in-Chief of the Spanish Navy – Don John of Austria, who was Philip's half-brother. Ruy's tact and judgment had been invaluable to the King in all matters concerning Don John since they first discovered his existence ten years ago.

Philip's father, the Emperor Charles V, had left a letter for his heir as a codicil to his will. 'I say and declare,' it ran, 'that when I was in Germany and being a widower, I had, by an unmarried woman, a natural son who is called Jerome, and that my intention has been and is that he should, of his free and spontaneous will, take the habit of some order of friars, and that he should be put in the way of so doing, but without any pressure being employed. If he prefers a secular life, it is my pleasure and command that he should receive each year, from the revenues of the Kingdom of Naples, twenty to thirty thousand ducats, lands and vassals with that rent attached being assigned to him. The whole matter, both as to the assignment of the lands and the account of the rent, is left to the discretion of my son Philip to whom I remit it or, failing him, to the discretion of my grandson, Carlos, and whatever state the said Jerome shall embrace I charge my son and grandson, whichever shall be my heir, to do him honour and cause him to be honoured and that they show him fitting respect and that they observe, fulfil and execute in his favour what is contained in this paper.' To this the Emperor had added in his own hand: 'Son, grandson, whichever may be my heir when my will is opened, if you do not know where this Jerome may be, you can learn it from Adrian, groom of my chamber, or, in case of his death, from Oger, the porter of my chamber.'

The Emperor had 'Jerome' placed in the charge of the major-domo of his household, Don Luis de Quijada, head of a noble family in Old Castile whose seat was at Villagarcía, near Valladolid. When the boy was about four, he was taken into the household of the Emperor's favourite violinist (who was told that he was the bastard of Adrian de Bues, groom of His Majesty's chamber) at Leganés, a village just off the road from Madrid to Toledo. The parish priest was entrusted with his education – without being told who he was.

At Leganés the population consisted almost entirely of peasants who worked the land round the village and when, at the age of seven, Jerome was sent to the school at Getafe, three miles away, he went there as a rustic child among other country children on terms of complete equality with them. Quijada realised that unless the boy was to assume peasanthood he must be removed to surroundings more appropriate to his status and, with the Emperor's permission, took him into his own household at Villagarcía and gradually introduced him to Court. When the Emperor abdicated in favour of Philip and retired to the monastery of

Yuste, the boy was lodged in an anteroom of Quijada's apartments there and went in and out of the Emperor's room 'as he pleased'. He also managed to organise apple-stealing expeditions outside the walls and was pelted by local farmers, but the Emperor expressed satisfaction to Quijada on the way he had been brought up. No one, of course, knew who he was except the Emperor, Quijada, Adrian the groom and Oger the porter of the Royal Chamber. Even Quijada's wife, who treated him like a son, was under the impression that he was really her husband's bastard (though she accepted the agreed story that he was Adrian's), until one night a fire broke out at their castle at Villagarcía and Quijada rescued Jerome before attempting to save her, explaining that the boy was of such outstanding importance that he must be the first to be saved.

In those days at Court, Jerome, as a kind of page-extraordinary, occasionally played with King Philip's son, Don Carlos, who, though his nephew, was about eighteen months his senior, but he did not like him. The Emperor, too, was disturbed by his grandson's wayward and over-bearing temper and, at the same time as he congratulated Quijada on Jerome's upbringing, warned that unless Don Carlos were subjected to much sterner discipline, Spain might suffer for it.

During the Emperor's last days, King Philip was absent from the country, engaged in the French war, so that it was not until the September of 1559, that he met for the first time the brother of whose existence he had been unaware until he read his father's will.

To minimise the difficulties of protocol, it was decided that the meeting should take place in a wood while the King was hunting. Quijada made the necessary arrangements and, after telling his wife who Jerome was, set out with the twelve-year-old boy, and, at the agreed time and place, dismounted and told his charge to do the same. He then knelt down in front of the boy and asked permission to kiss his hand. After some hesitation the puzzled youth agreed, imagining this to be some recondite game. Quijada said: 'The King himself will tell you why I do this,' and beckoned to one of his grooms who led a fresh horse, splendidly caparisoned. When told to mount it Jerome, hoping that he was properly entering into the spirit of the game, said: 'Well, since you kiss my hand, you can also hold my stirrup,' which, somewhat to his surprise, his guardian did.

Almost immediately, the King, attended by Ruy Gómez and a few other courtiers, appeared and Quijada ordered his charge to kiss the King's hand. The boy's state of confusion was intensified when Philip, looking at him searchingly, asked: 'Do you know who your father was?' The boy was too abashed to say anything, but Philip answered the question by taking him in his arms and saying: 'You are the son of a great man. The Emperor Charles V who is now in Heaven was the father of both of us. Never have I hunted game more to my liking.'

To his courtiers Philip presented his brother as 'His Excellency Don John of Austria, natural son of the Emperor-King', and they all returned to Valladolid where a special establishment near the palace had been prepared for this belated addition to the Royal Family who in the future – except that he was 'Excellency', not 'Highness', and did not sit within the curtains of the royal tribune of the Chapel Royal – was to be treated as an Infante of Castile. Don John was to long for this final seal to his acceptance as his father's son – but his later achievements awoke his brother's suspicion and even enmity, and it was always refused him.

Meanwhile it was the then Prince of Asturias who found his arrival most disturbing. Don Carlos was at that time Philip's only son, born of his first wife Mary of Portugal, who had died giving birth to him. It was Don Carlos who found the change most disturbing. To discover that an obscure page eighteen months his junior was in fact his uncle was itself distracting enough, without the overnight appearance of what was, in effect, a younger brother to compete with in his father's affection. Even worse was the King's attitude. On one occasion the boys were quarrelling and Don Carlos shouted: 'I cannot argue with an inferior. Your mother was a whore and you are a bastard.' 'At any rate,' retorted Don John, 'my father was a greater man than yours.' Carlos rushed off to report this to the King who, to his discomfiture, answered: 'Don John is quite right. His father and mine was a far greater man than yours ever has been or ever will be.' And when, some days later, Don John asked his brother what he should do if Don Carlos attacked him physically, Philip replied: 'Forget that he is my son.'

The two boys were educated together and at first Don John (who, as Quijada had to report, 'disliked nothing as much as his studies in which he proceeds with difficulty'), had to accept the regimen of the celebrated Royal Governess, Doña Catalina de Cardona.

Doña Catalina was the daughter of the Duke of Cardona. Though she was born and brought up on her father's estates in Naples (the King of Spain was independently King of Naples and the Two Sicilies), she had come to grace the Spanish court some years before Don Carlos was born. An outstanding character by virtue of her strength of will, her aristocratic certainty and her stern piety, she was eventually chosen as Governess to the Infante, Don Carlos. Philip's sister, who was naturally in charge of the motherless boy during the King's frequent absences from Spain, tended to spoil him on the grounds of his delicate health, with the unfortunate results his grandfather had noticed; but Doña Catalina, who never spared herself, saw no reason to spare her charge. By the time he was eight, he had to be up at seven. By half-past eight he had heard Mass and had his breakfast. He then began his studies which lasted till eleven, when he dined. After exercise, in the form of riding and fencing, there was a light meal at half-past three, followed by more study, supper and bed at half-past nine.

Virtually the same curriculum was extended to include Don John, but within a year the King decided to send the two boys to the new university of Alcalá (where, unlike the great universities of Valladolid and Salamanca, the lectures were given in Latin instead of the vernacular). They were housed together in the empty palace of the Primates of Spain and put under the supervision of a noted educationist, Honorato Juan.

In accordance with his father's will, Don John was to be prepared for a career in the Church (Philip asked the Pope to make him a cardinal by way of encouragement), and Don Carlos was to be educated as became one whose destiny was to inherit the greatest kingdom in the world. Neither, however, showed any interest which would distinguish them from the conventional run of first-year undergraduates enjoying new-found freedom.

They had not been many months at the university when Don Carlos, running down a staircase to keep an assignation with the porter's daughter, missed his footing, fell down the last four or five steps and struck his head so violently on the corner of a door at the bottom that he was found insensible and in a critical condition. His father immediately rushed down to Alcalá from Madrid and agonisingly remained with him while every kind of medical skill was exercised in vain. When the doctors had to admit that the Infante was indubitably dying, Philip in despair ordered a last desperate expedient.

A hundred years previously there had died at Alcalá a certain Fray Diego, a Franciscan lay-brother of such holiness that he was reputed to have worked miracles of healing both before and after his death. His incorrupt body was a treasured relic of Alcalá and the King now obtained ecclesiastical permission for it to be carried and laid on the bed beside his insensible son. The dying boy immediately recovered.*

The return to health was not happy in its consequences. The sequel to the miracle – if such it was – included the making of Don Carlos the cynosure of all eyes and the centre of all Court gossip, which fed his megalomania and left it an open question whether his behaviour before or after his accident was the more intolerable. The most charitable explanation was that his fall had permanently damaged his brain; the more perceptive that his essential character revealed itself the more he had opportunities for self-assertion.

One of the many episodes widely discussed concerned a pair of boots. Carlos ordered the Royal bootmaker to make him some so large at the top that they would accommodate a pair of pistols. The King on hearing of it told the man to make them of a more conventional size. Don Carlos, on receiving them, not only severely beat the man, but ordered the leather to be cut into strips and stewed and given to him to eat.

Of the Infante's general conduct, a visitor from the French court recorded that he would roam the streets in the company of young hooligans kissing any attractive girls and hurling opprobrious epithets at the wives of respectable citizens.

In a desperate hope that responsibility might effect a change in him, the King appointed his son President of the Council of State. The result was that Carlos certainly became interested in political affairs which he had hitherto shunned but also that he saw the dangerous situation in the Netherlands merely as an ideal opportunity for his own aggrandisement. At that point there was still doubt as to

* At Philip's request, the Vatican instituted a process for Fray Diego's canonisation. It took twenty-five years to sift the evidence, but in 1588 the Franciscan lay-brother was raised to the altars of the Church as St. Didacus. His feast-day is 13 November.

whether the King himself should go to Brussels. It was proposed in the Cortes that, should this happen, the Infante, as the heir, should remain in Spain. Don Carlos thereupon threatened with death any deputy who should vote in favour of the motion; and when eventually it was decided that the Duke of Alba should be sent to Flanders to conduct the inquiry, the Prince lost all control and physically assaulted him.

This too-characteristic behaviour was motivated by a hope that he might, by offering himself as a leader or, more precisely, a figure-head to the rebels, obtain the Netherlands for himself. Though Alba's arrival in Brussels in the summer of 1567 might seem to have ended the possibility, Don Carlos continued his schemes and, on Christmas Eve, confided to Don John that he was on the point of secretly leaving Spain for Germany where a force was being collected for the Protestant invasion of the Low Countries.

Don Carlos was under the impression that Don John would welcome the opportunity of accompanying him because in the previous year when an expedition was being prepared to defend Malta against an attack by the Turks, Don John had pleaded to be allowed to leave the university and join it; and when the King had refused on the ground that he was 'much too young' he had slipped away with two attendants and made his way to Barcelona where the Spanish fleet was mustering. The fleet, however, had sailed before he arrived and a formal order from Philip, threatening him with disgrace unless he returned immediately, brought him back to Madrid where his escapade had already enhanced his reputation.

It was an indication of Don Carlos's unintelligence that he should equate Don John's action in attempting adventurously to join what was in effect a Spanish crusade against the Mohammedan enemies of the Faith with his own intention of heading an heretical rebellion against the Catholic King, his father. Don John, after vehement arguments, was unable to move his nephew and, in view of the gravity of the situation, considered that, whatever the consequences, he must warn his brother. Philip was spending Christmas at El Escorial and on Christmas Eve Don John rode over to give him his heartbreaking news.

Torn between his feelings as a father and his duty as King, Philip, on the advice of Ruy Gómez, convened a small panel of jurists and theologians including his own confessor to advise a proper course of action. The situation was adjudged the more dangerous because of the attitude of Don Carlos to the Mass which the Royal Family was accustomed to attend every year on the Feast of the Holy Innocents, 28 December. In his confession in preparation for this, Don Carlos said that he had a mortal enemy whom he could not forgive and whom he intended to kill, if possible. The priest had to refuse him absolution. Carlos then went to the Royal Jeronymite monastery, explained his position and asked for a confessor who would absolve him, so that he might receive Holy Communion with the rest on Innocents' Day. Twelve theologians were summoned, all of whom, naturally, agreed that the thing was impossible. He then additionally scandalised them by suggesting that arrangements might be made to give them an unconsecrated Host when he knelt at the altar with his father, his brother and the rest of his family. During these conversations, he revealed that the person he intended to kill was the King, his father.

The verdict of the panel was that Don Carlos 'who had not given proofs of such obedient, quiet and prudent qualities as there is need for in the Heir to the Throne', but, on the contrary, 'wished to have his own way and to be in command in everything', must be prevented from leaving the country, since his departure in the existing circumstances might plunge Europe into war and possibly ruin the Spanish Empire and its inhabitants. The King had thus a duty to take whatever measures were considered necessary to restrain the son.

In consequence, on the night of 17 January 1568, while Don Carlos was asleep, the King, attended by his confessor, Ruy Gómez and three other gentlemen of the court and twelve guards, entered his son's bedroom to arrest him.

Carlos screamed: 'So you have come to kill me!' (or was it, 'So *you* have come to kill *me*!'?).

Philip said: 'Calm yourself, my son. I have no wish but for your own good and Spain's. But you must come with me.' He took him to a special wing of the palace he had had prepared for him, where he was confined to his own room, with all his usual servants to wait on him. On 2 March, most of these were dismissed and the Prince and Princess of Eboli were given charge of him and installed in a temporary residence next to that of the Prince. A hole was made in the wall, so that Don Carlos could see and hear Mass in the adjoining chapel.

Two halberdiers were on guard outside the door with orders to admit only the King or Ruy Gómez or those they might send. Six *monteros* took the Infante's food to an outer chamber, whence it was carried to him by the young men of noble blood appointed to attend on him. They treated him with the strict deference due to his rank and none of them was allowed to bear arms of any description since he was unarmed. They had to taste his food, as a precaution against poison, and were to see to the cleanliness of his clothes and his room. They were also to see he was provided with books, including books of orthodox devotion. At the outset, the prisoner accepted his fate with at least an appearance of resignation. On Easter Day – 18 April 1568 – he made his confession, received communion and seemed reconciled to his fate.

But with the intolerable summer heat came alternate bouts of rage and despair. He drank huge quantities of icy water from a great fountain of snow, chilled his bed with it and splashed in it barefoot on the floor. Having tried to starve himself to death, he swallowed a diamond ring with suicidal purpose. After this attempt he refused to get out of bed for weeks, changing his position every moment, 'which would kill the most robust', as one observer put it. Then, for three days he lay motionless, staring at the ceiling as one bereft of all hope, until the King came and comforted him.

Carlos then resumed eating. After bolting several dishes with his old-time voracity, he devoured the whole of a highly-spiced partridge-pie, with the result that he 'became gravely ill with malignant double-tertian fever, vomiting and diarrhoea'.

The doctors now pronounced the illness mortal and begged the King to see his son before he died, but the Prince's confessor, Fray Diego de Chaves, and his old tutor, Honorato Juan, both agreed that the sight of Philip might have an unfortunate effect on him. He had forgiven his father and was disposed to die a Christian death. But knowing how quickly his rages came upon him, the two good old men were afraid that the sight of the King might undo all their good work and even cause him to die in anger and sin.

Philip acquiesced, but during the evening he quietly entered his son's room, walking behind Ruy Gómez and the prior Don Antonio. When they reached the bedside, he raised his hand between the shoulders of the two men and gave Don Carlos his blessing. Then 'he shut himself in his room with more sorrow but less worry and waited for news of the end'.

It came at four o'clock in the afternoon of the Vigil of St. James, Patron Saint of Spain, 24 July 1568. According to an eyewitness, 'the necessary arrangements for the funeral pomp were made the same day and they went out with the body at seven o'clock in the evening. The casket was of lead, inside another of wood and it was very heavy, and they bore it on some poles, litter-wise, covered with a cloth of brocade. The body reposed in state under a magnificent *baldachino* in the black-draped church of Saint Dominic el Real until 12 August (the day after the Feast of St. Lawrence), when it was intered with great pomp'. Philip was not present. He was at El Escorial, to which, in due time, the body of Don Carlos was transferred, to lie in the Panteón de los Infantes.

The news of the Infante's death set Madrid afire with scandal. Many if not most of the people affected to believe that the King had had his son murdered.* Some believed that Carlos had done away with himself. There was talk of rivalry in love between father and son for the young Queen Elizabeth of Valois, who, three months later, died in childbirth. After this event, Ruy Gómez said that the deaths of his only son and his greatly-loved wife, coming so closely together, made Philip suddenly an old man, though he was only in fact forty-one; and many besides Ruy were shocked by the change in his appearance.

* Over a century later, Saint-Simon, visiting the Escorial, records: 'Passing the end of the vault, we descried the coffin of Don Carlos. I told our *cicerone* that the King (of France), soon after his arrival in Spain, had the curiosity to have the coffin of Don Carlos opened, and I myself, knowing an eye-witness of the scene – Liouville – he informed me that the head was found between the legs; that Philip II, his father, had it cut off before him in his prison. "Ah, well!" cried the monk furiously, "it probably served him right, as King Philip had the Pope's permission." '

This anecdote, though hardly evidence one way or the other of Philip's guilt, fairly represents contemporary and near-contemporary feeling. Today opinion – for there can be nothing but opinion – has come round to Philip's side.

III
A Career for Don John

Don John also was sufficiently affected by the course of events to retire into the Franciscan friary at Abrojo, not far from Valladolid, which was noted for its austerities. In this decision he was not unaffected by the conduct of Doña Catalina, his and Carlos's former Governess.

After the boys had been taken from her charge and sent to the university, Doña Catalina had grown increasingly dissatisfied with life at Court and when Don Carlos was miraculously restored – for she had no doubt that it was a miracle – after his accident, she resolved to devote herself to a life of penance to expiate the sins of the Court. Her confessor tried to dissuade her from going to the extreme lengths she contemplated, but on one occasion when she was visiting the Franciscans at Alcalá she prevailed on one of the brothers to accompany her to another Franciscan house about a hundred miles away, which was renowned, like that of Abrojo, for its austerities. With them on the journey went Ruy Gómez's chaplain, Don Martín Alonso, on the orders of Ruy, who hoped that on the way Doña Catalina might change her mind at least to the extent of entering a convent. Ruy himself had little real hope of it, since Ana, his wife, who was one of Catalina's friends at Court, had originally suggested it to her, only to be met by: 'I am certainly not going to live among affected, sentimental sugary nuns whose imaginations make our natural weaknesses worse.'

When the travellers reached the environs of the friary at La Roda Catalina found a little cave 'so small that she could hardly get into it', and made it her home. After she had finished the bread that her companions had left her (which, at her insistence, was only three loaves), she lived on plants and roots she gathered in the fields until one day a shepherd-boy discovered her. Thereafter he used to supply her with bread and flour, with which she would make little cakes, baking them on a wood fire. Of these, which formed the whole of her meals, she partook every third day. The friars who, once her cave was discovered, paid her occasional visits found her 'very wasted' and, when they could, induced her to 'eat a sardine or something'. She found it did her more harm than good.

'For discipline,' wrote one who knew her, 'she wore a heavy chain, often for as long as an hour and a half or two hours on end. Her hair shirts were very rough, as I was told by a woman who, when returning from a pilgrimage, had stayed with her for one night and, while pretending to be asleep, had seen her take off her hair shirt, which was soaked with blood, and wash it. She would attend Mass at the Mercedarian monastery, a quarter of a league distant, and sometimes she would go there on her knees. Her dress was of kersey and her tunic of frieze and was made in such a way that people thought she was a man.'

Don John's ascetic practices among the Franciscans at Abrojo were only a little less famed for their austerity than those of Catalina de Cardona. However, the stresses to which Don John subjected his body had as their object not penance but the perfecting of himself as a soldier. Whatever his father may have wished for him he had no doubt now that soldiering was his true vocation and that he could exercise it as a latter-day crusader in defence of the Faith. A week before Christmas events seemed to confirm this ambition.

A detachment of fifty Spanish soldiers were murdered in

their beds in a small village near Granada. The killers were Moriscoes – Moors who had become nominal Christians seventy-five years before when Ferdinand and Isabella regained the land for Christianity – but who had remained at heart true to Islam. In fact, 'they were', a contemporary observed, 'more zealous Mohammedans than the very Moors born in Barbary'; and now that the Mediterranean was menaced by the Turks under Suleiman the Magnificent, they were planning an insurrection to assist their co-religionists. It was, however, premature, and their attempt to take Granada was unsuccessful, although for a short time on the day after Christmas the streets echoed with the cry: 'There is one God and Mohammed is his prophet.'

When Don John at Abrojo heard the report of these happenings, he wrote immediately to his brother asking to be appointed to command an expedition against them: 'As some person must be sent thither and my nature leads me to these pursuits and I am as obedient to Your Majesty's royal will as the clay to the hand of the potter, it appeared to me that I should be wanting in love and inclination and duty if I did not offer myself for this post. Although I know that those who serve Your Majesty are safe in your royal hands and ought not to ask, yet I trust that what I have done may be considered rather a merit than a fault. To this end I came from Abrojo which, but for the sake of Your Majesty's service and the importance of the occasion, I should not have ventured to do.'

After some hesitation on account of his brother's youthfulness – he was twenty-one – the King granted his request and Don John, now General of the Sea, proceeded to Granada to put down the rebellion. But once in the field, his impetuosity troubled Philip. 'I heard the other day, with regret,' the King was constrained to write, 'that you have been out with a skirmishing expedition. This does not befit you, nor is it your duty, which is to watch over the city. Even if the Duke of Sesa and Luis Quijada go with you it is not right. You also go and visit the sentinels and watch the patrols on their rounds. This should not be done by you too often. Only from time to time when circumstances require it.'

'If I had more experience and practice in my profession,' Don John replied, 'I should have nothing to say, but as I am only learning the service in which I hope to die, I must not miss what opportunities there are of improving myself in it. I entreat you to observe how little it befits me, being what I am and my age, to shut myself up when I ought to be showing myself abroad.'

Philip answered: 'You must keep yourself and I must keep you for greater things and it is from these that you must learn your professional knowledge.'

'I am certainly most desirous to give satisfaction to Your Majesty and do in all things as you wish,' replied Don John, 'but as I see it, Your Majesty's interest requires that when there is a call to arms or any enterprise, the soldiers should find me in front of them – or at least with them – ready to encourage them to do their duty; and that they should know that I am leading them in the name of Your Majesty.'

The King was, in fact, afraid for his brother's life. *That* death to crown his other bereavements was not to be thought of; and when, in the summer of 1569, he summoned Ruy Gómez to El Escorial, it was to consult him as to the best way to restrain Don John from taking unnecessary risks.

Ruy, who had always been able to speak frankly to Don John, wrote to him immediately: 'You Excellency is said to be rash and more desirous to obtain a reputation as a soldier than as a general. You know well that everyone ought to do his own duty and not the general the soldier's or the soldier the general's. Pray let this be changed!'

Don John in reply assured Gómez that he was grateful for his advice and that no criticism from him could ever come amiss. He hoped that Ruy would always speak and write with absolute frankness, since there was no one he trusted more. 'I can assure you, Sir, that as regards what you advise about my doing my duty rather as a general than as a soldier, I will keep it in mind and never forget it.'

Nevertheless the circumstances of the war made it, as he saw it, impossible always to behave as he was expected to. In one assault the Spanish troops got out of hand and a counter-attack by the Moriscoes was on the point of succeeding. Don John, seeing what was happening, rode into the stream of fugitives and, reining his horse across their path, shouted: 'Soldiers! what are you fleeing from? Where is the honour of Spain? Turn and face this barbarous rabble and you will soon see it in flight before you!' He saved the day, but while he was speaking, he was struck by a musket ball and only saved from death by the strength of his helmet, while Quijada, who was, as always, beside him, received a wound from an arquebus-shot from which, either because of the seriousness of the wound or the incompetence of his doctors, he died a week later.

The news drew from the King his sternest reprimand: 'This has given me more pain than I can tell you. I now definitely *order* you, and shall take it very ill if you disobey my order, to remain in the place which befits one who has charge of this business, and is moreover my brother. You are not to risk your life as you have been doing. I speak to you as one who loves you, as it is right that I should, and desires that you should behave in all things as the son of our father.'

Philip before sending it showed the letter to Ruy, who said bluntly: 'He will wish to obey, but he will not be able to.'

'Why?'

'Because of his nature; because he is born that way.'

After a long discussion, the King and his minister and friend decided that Don John could only be influenced by someone who was actually at his side.

'I cannot be there myself and I cannot send you, Ruy. Have you anyone in mind?'

Ruy Gómez, for a moment, thought of recommending Pérez or Escovedo, but quickly decided that the one would never be able to gain Don John's confidence and the other was not mature enough for the situation. But he had a third secretary, Juan de Soto, who would be admirable. Though he had no desire to lose him, he realised that the situation was desperate and before the month was out de Soto was on the way to Granada, bearing a letter of introduction from Ruy: 'He is a man with whom Your Excellency may well take counsel on all matters. I entreat you to show him the favour he deserves, for I promise you he is a great treasure and a man for bringing whom to your acquaintance you will one day give me many thanks.'

Gómez had no doubt that de Soto, if he proved *persona grata* to Don John, would unobtrusively steer the unbiddable young soldier into courses which would be to everyone's satisfaction and to the best interests and honour of Spain.

Confident that he had given the King the best possible advice, he rode back satisfied to Pastrana where Ana was waiting for him. He could not know that within ten years the pattern of diplomatic control he had initiated would lead to Ana's imprisonment, Escovedo's murder and Don John's death.

IV
The Last Crusade

Don John, when his new secretary arrived to take up his duties in the spring of 1570, was a puzzled and uncertain young man. In an unusually frank letter to the widow of Luis de Quijada, whom he treated as his mother, he bared his heart. He had heard it rumoured that his brother, the King, intended to send him to the Netherlands to replace Alba. 'In this case,' he wrote, 'I should stand out against it. It would not suit me at all. For one thing it is so far away.' There was also the high matter of the Pope's call for the formation of a Holy League as a last crusade to rid Christendom of the Mohammedan menace which had bedevilled it for a century. 'I have just received a letter from the King, my brother, written in his own hand in which he tells me of the need he has of me for this affair of the League and other matters. I shall believe what I shall see. Your ladyship tells me, with your great and wonted kindness, to consider carefully what I do, because all eyes are now fixed on me, and not to be too adventurous, but rather to avoid all occasions of risk. I will endeavour to steer my course as well as I can in conformity with the advice of your ladyship, for there is no one whom I so much desire to satisfy as her to whom I owe my bringing-up and the place in the world which I now hold – obligations which I shall acknowledge even in my grave.'

In the event, Don John was chosen as Commander-in-Chief of both land and sea forces of the Holy League which, after more than a year of diplomatic haggling, bound Spain, Venice and the Papacy together in what in fact became the last of the crusades. On the Feast of St. James, the Patron Saint of Spain, the Holy League was publicly inaugurated in Rome, and on the previous day – 24 July 1571 – the Pope wrote to Don John, congratulating him upon his appointment: 'To our well-beloved son in Christ, health and the Apostolic Benediction! Almighty God, the author of all good, has been pleased that, by His divine favour, the League should be concluded which I, your brother, the Catholic King of the Spains, and the Illustrious Republic of the Venetians some months ago began to negotiate against that most cruel tyrant, the Lord of the Turks. As it has come to so satisfactory an issue, it seems right to congratulate your nobility on the occasion, as by this letter we do, being certain that our message will be welcome and agreeable to you on account both of your piety towards God and of your desire for the increase of the Christian world.'

This conventional formality in fact expressed the simple truth in the meeting of two men who temperamentally complemented each other, the 24-year-old soldier, who was to reveal himself an unrivalled leader of men, and the 67-year-old St. Pius V, one of the most courageous Popes of that or any century.

Pius was the son of a corn dealer and in his boyhood he used to travel with the mules that carried the grain from his home in Lombardy across the Ligurian Alps to the Mediterranean ports. When he was fourteen he became a Dominican friar and his active brain ensured that his rise, in that most intellectual of Orders, was rapid. He prepared the best edition of the works of the great philosopher of the Order, St. Thomas Aquinas, and himself lectured on philosophy for sixteen years at the leading European university, Bologna, as well as being appointed Inquisitor-General – to prevent him, as he remarked ruefully, from returning to the peace of the cloister.

What impressed all who came in contact with him – second only to his fervent goodness which led to the popular belief that he could obtain from God anything he asked – was his practicality and force of character. On one occasion, when three hundred hungry soldiers threatened to sack the friary of which he was prior unless they were given food, he calmly organised them and let them work on the farms and established such an ascendancy over them that they not only carried out any orders he gave them and protected the house from marauders, but when they finally departed left a large offering in acknowledgement of the hospitality of St. Dominic.

On the occasion of his coronation, Pius saw to it that the customary largesse was not scattered indiscriminately but was bestowed on hospitals and the really poor, while the money which was usually spent in providing banquets for ambassadors, cardinals and other eminent personages, was sent to the poorer convents of Rome.

To his unyielding courage was united the simplicity of great learning, which cut through the meshes of sentimentality and expediency to the core of reality. He could have adopted the cry of Roland, fighting the infidels: 'Christians are right; pagans are wrong.'

He assumed the burden of the Church at a moment when its very survival from the attacks of Protestants within and Mohammedans without seemed in doubt. But he never wavered in his aggressive resistance to both. Though it would have been diplomatic wisdom to gain the goodwill of England for the Holy League, he insisted on excommunicating Queen Elizabeth (in spite of two protests against such a step by King Philip) as 'a heretic and an abettor of heretics' and pronouncing her co-religionists 'to have incurred the sentence of anathema and to be cut off from the unity of Christ's body'.

Within the Church, he enforced the decrees of the Council of Trent with such vigour that the equivocations of crypto-Protestantism which were crippling it were rooted out for four centuries.* He expelled the usurious and brothel-keeping Jews from Rome, 'not because he was cruel but because he could not face the choice of incurring the charge of rigour or of allowing his people to be exploited and destroyed. His administration was like a strong medicine to restore the health of Christendom. Its reaction on unhealthy tissue was often unpleasant, but it accomplished its purpose'. As for himself, the burden seemed so intolerable that he said God had placed it on him in punishment of his sins (he had never wished to be Pope) but he behaved unflinchingly as his conscience commanded.

During the diplomatic exchanges which accompanied the formation of the League, Pius alone refused to be intimidated by the magnitude of the enterprise. The Turks were vulnerable. They had lost eighteen major battles during their century-long aggression. Only God was invincible. The Christian Princes were much to blame by their lack of trust, by their inertia and by their spreading of alarmist rumours. Let them now repent before it was too late and atone for their faults by uniting in defence of the Church. Let no more be heard of the impossibility of defeating the infidel in open battle upon the sea. 'Turn your eyes to Christ, the only Giver of Victory!'

Such was the man who, by the hand of a cardinal-ambassador in the conventual church of St. Clara in Naples on 14 August 1571, delivered to Don John the standard of the League. It was of blue damask and in the centre was a superbly-worked image of Christ Crucified. Beneath this were linked together the scutcheon of the Pope – three blood-red bars on a silver field – the lion shield of Venice and a shield bearing the elaborate quarterings of King Philip of Spain. Lower still, the design ended in the arms of Don

* They have been restored by the present Pope in a bull (1969) specifically abrogating St. Pius's decree.

John himself. As Captain-General of the League, he was henceforth to use no personal banner, but only this of his new office.

On the steps of the high altar, it was presented to him with the words: 'Take, fortunate Prince, these emblems of the Word-Made-Flesh, these symbols of the True Faith and may they give you a glorious victory over our impious enemy, and by your hand may his pride be laid low!'

'Amen!' replied Don John, to be echoed by everyone present.

Don John's duty, as he saw it, was to bring to battle the huge Turkish fleet which dominated the Mediterranean and which had recently attacked the island of Cyprus, held for the Christians by the Venetians under Marc Antonio Bragadino. Eventually hunger forced Bragadino to surrender Famagusta to Lala Mustapha Pasha, the Turkish commander who was besieging this last Christian fort on the island. The terms were generous, since it was known that Don John was about to set sail and Lala Mustapha had no wish to be caught between the fires of the Famagusta garrison and the forces of the League. All lives were to be spared; the entire garrison was to be transported, with their arms and property, to Crete and the ordinary inhabitants could either remain in safety in Cyprus or go unmolested wherever they wished.

Once Bragadino had surrendered on these terms, the Turk had all the Venetians massacred, the native Cypriots sold into slavery and the chief ones tortured and butchered, women as well as men. Bragadino himself was imprisoned and tortured for a fortnight, at the end of which time he was bound to a pillory in the square of Famagusta and flayed alive under the eyes of the Pasha. His skin, stuffed with straw, was exposed to public ridicule and eventually sent to Constantinople for the delectation of the Sultan, Selim the Sot. In the interim, it was at the moment swinging from the yardarm of Lala Mustapha's flagship as, with the rest of the three hundred sail of the 'invincible' Turkish armada, it roamed the Mediterranean in search of the Christians.

Meanwhile Don John, after staying only three days in Naples, sailed for Messina in Sicily, which had been appointed the rendezvous for all the forces of the League. Here he was joined by the Venetians, under the able but testy Sebastian Veniero, the 75-year-old Governor of Crete; by the Papal forces, commanded by Marcantonio Colonna; and by the Genoese squadron under Andrea Doria, Prince of Genoa, which King Philip had hired as an addition to the Spanish fleet.

Doria (whom the Pope disliked and distrusted as being no better than one of the Barbary corsairs he had spent his life fighting), had been appointed by King Philip as one of the three men without whose permission Don John was to take no major action. The other two were Don Luis de Requesens, who had been appointed Vice-Admiral and was the son of Philip's tutor, Zúñiga (in their youth, Requesens had once unhorsed Philip at a tournament so effectively that for some moments he had been thought to be dead) and Don Alvaro de Bazán, Marquis of Santa Cruz, who, at forty-five – a year older than Philip – was undoubtedly the foremost seaman of Europe. Both men had originally been appointed to train Don John in seamanship when he was given his first command and, in a sense, it was natural that the King, with his unalterable opinion of his brother's 'rashness', should still rely on them to act as a restraining influence on Don John. And nowhere, perhaps, was Philip's chronic misjudgment of men and situations more dangerous.

For Requesens, who was always at Don John's elbow 'to keep an eye on him' even at meals, the young Prince developed a strong dislike; and though he admired and trusted Santa Cruz, he was cut to the quick by Philip's appointment of 'overseers'. Early that July, he had written directly about it to Ruy Gómez, asking for his advice and reminding him 'how meritorious it is before God to act the part of a father to one who has no other father but you' and explaining that he was 'beset by a thousand persons who seek occasion in my youth and inexperience to ruin me, as if ruining me would be for their honour and advantage'.

'I confess to you,' the letter ran, 'that the unkind treatment of putting me on an equality with many others at a time when everyone seems to be observing me at times leads me to think of giving up my post and seeking some other path in which to serve God and His Majesty. It is being made so clear to me that I am not considered fit for the position that has been given me. The only thing that consoles me is the thought that, as I do not really deserve the treatment I am getting, it originates not with His Majesty but with someone at Court who tells him that if I am allowed no real power, his own authority will appear the greater.'

Ruy Gómez could not pretend to misunderstand the reference. He himself was watching with some apprehension the complete conquest which his own one-time secretary, Antonio Pérez, was making of the King now that he had been transferred to Philip's personal service. Pérez was obviously determined to rule the ruler. But Ruy, who was ill and wished only to retire to spend his last days at Pastrana, was not concerned to obstruct it. His own position with the King was completely unassailable. He had some sympathy, as well as increasing admiration and affection for Don John. But the young man would have to learn to fight his own battles, at court as well as at sea. Ruy had approved the extent to which he had won over the new secretary, de Soto, whom they had given him to influence his judgments. It would do no harm to anyone, Ruy decided, to suggest that Don John should make his complaint direct to the King.

Don John was the more willing to do so because, on the eve of sailing for Naples, he had received a long missive from Antonio Pérez, in the King's name, enclosing a copy of Philip's instructions to the various Spanish ambassadors in Italy on matters of protocol and containing a reminder that, though Commander-in-Chief, he was to risk no engagement without the unanimously expressed approval of Doria, Requesens and Santa Cruz.

'Your Majesty has done me a very great favour', he wrote, 'in directing Antonio Pérez to send me a copy of the instructions sent to the ministers in Italy on how I am to be received and treated. Not only will it be a pleasure to me to conform myself to Your Majesty's will in this, as in all matters, but I should be glad to have the power of divining your thoughts in everything else in order to follow them as is my duty.

'Yet with due humility and respect, I venture to say it would be a great boon if Your Majesty would be pleased to communicate with me direct. I desire this for two reasons.

'The first and chief reason is that, in affairs of this quality it is not for the good of Your Majesty's service that any of your ministers should be put in such a position as to be able to argue with me as to what your pleasure is – none of them being under the obligation to give it effect which I am.

'The other reason is that I may have made some arrangements of my own which I would prefer not to be common knowledge. Also, inasmuch as God has made me Your Majesty's brother, I cannot avoid feeling hurt that you consider me so little that at a time when I might have been thought to have deserved something at your hands, I should have a proof to the contrary in your order reducing me to an equality with many others of your servants.

'God knows the pain which this has given me, merely because it shows how little satisfaction my services have given you. As a result I very often find myself thinking that it would please you better if I were to seek some other mode of serving you, since in my present position I believe myself to be so out of favour that I cannot accomplish what I strive for.

'Meanwhile I will endeavour to obey Your Majesty's orders, whatever they may be. On your part you must believe that I wish for neither honours nor wealth unless for the purpose of therewith serving you better. I shall not fail in my duty in any case whatever.'

In his heart, Philip did not doubt his brother's loyalty, however sceptical he might be of his ability. But it was expecting too much of human nature for the most powerful monarch in Europe (who, however, was and knew he was useless as a soldier) to recognise in his bastard brother, hardly more than half his age, a born leader of men.

The tension between the brothers was increased by the fact that the bastard had manifestly inherited their father's tastes and temperament whereas the heir noticeably lacked them. The Emperor Charles V had rejoiced in war. In the year of Don John's birth, when he was forty-seven, he had won the battle of Muhlberg* – and had been incessantly on the march with his troops, spending the night under canvas, on horseback all day, in spite of the pangs of gout. ('Field-life suits this prince particularly well,' it was reported.) The outstanding quality of Philip on the other hand was a love of peace and quietness and a corresponding abhorrence of violence. According to an observant Venetian, whereas Charles had made himself master of Christendom by his constant care to seize any opportunity to extend his power and estates, his heir was content to defend himself if attacked – and then only with some reluctance. 'He thinks less of increasing his own power than of obstructing the power of others and on the slightest apprehension he would prefer to surrender estates rather than fight for them. He is not a natural ruler, still less an autocrat, for he acts according

* A battle which may be compared in decisive importance to Europe in the sixteenth century with Blenheim in the eighteenth and Waterloo in the nineteenth; but not, for obvious reasons, so well known to English readers who nevertheless may know Titian's famous portrait of Charles on horseback at the battle.

to the advice of others. Here he esteems only the Spanish, taking little notice of Italians and Flemings and none at all of Germans.'

The Emperor also considered himself as the successor of Charlemagne, the leader of the Christians against the Mohammedans, and when Tunis was captured by the Turk, he had insisted that the danger to the Mediterranean involved all the Christian powers. The fleets which had assembled at Barcelona were those of Spain, Portugal, Genoa, the Papacy, and the Empire and when the various leaders had enquired who was to be commander-in-chief, the Emperor had raised a crucifix and answered: 'He whose standard-bearer I am.' He led the forces in person and when he returned in triumph to Messina, he was greeted with triumphal arches inscribed: 'To the founder of tranquillity and peace, the illustrious Charles, saviour of the fatherland, who drove off the Turks and preserved the Christian Republic, in memory of his glorious deeds in Africa, do the senate and people of Messina dedicate these triumphal arches and gates of honour.'

That was thirty-six years ago, well before Don John's birth, yet now when on 23 August 1571 Don John landed at Messina, it was as if there had been no interval. Even the time of year emphasised the continuity (Charles had entered Messina on 23 August 1535) and the son was but taking up his father's work.

In the harbour, in front of the landing place, there had been erected a huge, square edifice with broad steps descending to the water, while each of its sides displayed three triumphal arches adorned with inscriptions, based on those (if not, in some cases, actually the same, refurbished) which had greeted the Emperor; and as Don John passed up the steps and under the arches to receive a magnificent charger with silver trappings as a gift from the municipality of Messina while the people cheered themselves hoarse, it seemed for a moment that time had stood still.

Don John wrote to the man whose advice he valued and constantly asked – his predecessor in command of the navy, Don García of Toledo, who was now an ageing invalid taking the baths in Tuscany: 'Yesterday I began to visit the galleys of the Venetians. You cannot believe what bad order both soldiers and sailors were in. Arms and artillery they certainly have, but as fighting demands men, my blood runs cold when I see with what materials I am expected to do something of importance. Nevertheless, I will do my best, although no kind of order seems to prevail among them and each galley seems to come and go as its captain pleases.'

Don García's advice at this moment would be the more useful in that he had been with the Emperor on the Tunis campaign. What, asked Don John, was his opinion on the vexed question whether, in a naval battle, it was advisable to be the first to open fire?

The old admiral replied: 'In my judgment the troopers are right who say that you should never fire your arquebus until you are near enough to be splashed with the blood of your enemy; and I have always heard the most experienced sea-captains say that the crashing of the ship's iron beak and the first report of her guns should be heard at the same moment. I think so too. But your men should be taught not to be considering the enemy, or who is to fire first or last, but to fire when Your Highness gives the word and only then.'

When Requesens, also discussing tactics with Don García, made his usual complaint of Don John's youth and inexperience, he was met with the snub: 'By the life of St. Peter, I swear that if I had a little better health I would ship myself as a soldier or a sailor under Don John.'

When the whole Christian armament had assembled, Don John insisted on seeking the advice not only of the three specified by Philip (two of whom were in favour of continued delay) but of seventy officers who, at a meeting on his flagship, overwhelmingly endorsed his decision to sail immediately and bring the Turk to battle.

On the morning of 15 September the great fleet put to sea. As it passed into the open Mediterranean, the Papal Nuncio stood at the end of the mole, blessing each ship individually as it passed him, the men kneeling on the decks, a crucifix on every prow and Don John, in golden armour, with a fragment of the True Cross which the Pope had sent him for the occasion round his neck, standing on the flagship under the blue banner of Our Lady of Guadalupe (the Pope's standard was reserved for battle).

'Tonight I sail, please God, for Corfu,' he wrote to Don García. 'The enemy is stronger than we are, in the number of his vessels, but not so, I believe, in quality of men or ships. I have with me two hundred and eight galleys, twenty-six thousand troops, six galeasses and twenty-four other ships. I trust Our Lord that He will grant us victory if we meet the infidel.'

At Corfu, they found evidence that the infidel had been there before them. The fortress itself was still in Christian hands but in the outskirts the sight of charred and ruined churches, smashed altars and defiled crucifixes, pictures of the saints which had been used for target practice and the mangled and tortured bodies of priests left as food for vultures increased the crusaders' desire to come to grips with the Mohammedans as quickly as possible. Fortunately some scouts were able to give the information that the Turkish fleet, under Ali Pasha, the Sultan's brother-in-law, was assembling in the Gulf of Lepanto in preparation for a return to Constantinople before the onset of the autumn storms. On 30 September, Don John, once more with the general approval of his officers, sailed south and, using oars because the wind was contrary, accomplished the journey of a hundred miles or so to the mouth of the Gulf within five days. The long inlet from the Ionian Sea, extending from west to east, bounded on the north by the coast of Albania and on the south by that of the Peloponnese and closed at the eastern end by the Gulf of Corinth, was not far from Actium where west had so signally defeated east in the days of Cleopatra.

If this were an omen of interest only to the learned, some long-delayed news delivered by a brigantine from Candia, on 5 October, roused the entire fleet to a renewal of the crusading ardour which had swept it at Corfu. The two-months-old news was the story of the fall of Famagusta, the broken word, the subsequent atrocities of the infidel and the fate of Bragadino. It could not have come at a more appropriate moment. Bragadino's brother Augustin and his nephew were, under Viniero, in charge of the Venetian contingent of the fleet, commanding the left wing. Led by them every Venetian swore to give no quarter to any Turk in the battle to come. National honour reinforced religious loyalty and the human instinct for revenge. The Venetians could now be counted on to fight like holy madmen.

At two o'clock in the morning of Sunday, 7 October, a steady wind from the west rose suddenly and dispersed the fog which, for the best part of two days, had been obscuring the exact position of the fleet. Don John gave the word, sails were unfurled and by dawn the Christians were hardly twelve miles from the Mohammedan ships.

'Here we must conquer or die,' said Don John exultantly and, at daybreak, ordered a green banner to be displayed as a sign for all to get in battle array.

His secretary, Juan de Soto, asked dutifully, if not without a trace of irony: 'Is Your Highness going to call a Council of War?'

'Praise God,' was the quick answer, 'this is the time to fight not talk.'

His one fear was that the Turks might refuse battle, but as Ali Pasha had a superiority of 286 galleys to Don John's 208, the Turkish commander was eager for an engagement and, arranging his ships in the form of an immense crescent stretching right across the Gulf, started slowly to advance.

Don John, having appointed his order of battle and, on

account of his numerical inferiority, having increased the reserve under Santa Cruz from thirty to thirty-five with instructions to sail in the rear and reinforce any part of the line that seemed to need it, boarded the fastest of his brigantines and inspected the fleet, holding up a great iron crucifix, to which each crew knelt as he passed. On his return to his flagship, *La Real*, the Pope's banner of the Holy League was run up to the accompaniment of a tremendous, unbroken cheer so loud that it drowned for the moment the blood-curdling chorus of screams, hoots, jibes and groans from the Turks accompanied by the clashing of scimitars on shields, the blaring of horns and the firing of volleys of muskets into the air.

The opening shots were fired at about eleven o'clock and when battle was joined, the order was given by each commander-in-chief to steer direct for the flagship of the other – *La Real* against the *Sultana*. When the prow of the *Sultana* crashed into *La Real* it became entangled in the Spanish ship's rigging and thus linked together the ships became a battlefield which was fiercely contested for nearly two hours. Twice the Spaniards obtained a foot-hold on the *Sultana* and twice were driven back. Then Don John put himself at the head of the boarding party, while Ali fought at the head of the defenders. The Turkish commander was hit by a bullet in his forehead and fell forward on the gangway, whereupon a soldier cut off his head and took it to Don John, hoping for a great reward. Don John, however, was furiously angry, for he knew Ali Pasha's reputation for kindness to his Christian slaves, and merely said: 'What do you expect me to do with that head? Throw it into the sea.'

V

Lepanto and the Aftermath

In Rome, on the previous evening, the Pope had sent out special instructions that all the monasteries and convents were to redouble their prayers for the success of the Crusade and had himself led the saying of the Rosary at his own Dominican convent of the Minerva. On the afternoon of the Sunday, Pius was walking in the Vatican with his treasurer, Donato Cesis. Suddenly he stepped aside, opened a window and looked out, as if he was hearing some distant sound. Then he turned back to his companion, his face radiant, and dismissed him with: 'Go with God. This is no time for business, but for giving thanks to Jesus Christ, for at this moment our fleet is victorious.' St. Pius then hurried into the Sistine Chapel and prostrated himself in prayer before the Blessed Sacrament on the altar.

Not unnaturally the treasurer was sufficiently impressed to make careful note of the exact time, later to discover it was the moment that Ali Pasha fell.

News of the victory reached Rome through human agencies a fortnight later with the Count of Priego, Don John's official messenger, who travelled as far as Otranto in a fast Venetian galley and continued overland to Rome. The Pope greeted him with the words from the Gospel: 'There was a man from God whose name was John,' and in memory of the victory, added 'Help of Christians' to the titles of Our Lady in the Litany of Loreto and appointed 7 October as the Feast of the Holy Rosary as a reminder that during the battle the Procession of the Rosary in the church of the Minerva was ceaselessly praying for victory.*

Philip received news of the victory on the eve of All Saints (31 October). Don John gave him a full account of it, once the Christian fleet cast anchor in the harbour of Petala at dusk. The King was told of the estimated casualties – 113 Turkish galleys wrecked or sunk and 117 captured, with the freeing of 15,000 Christian galley-slaves; 30,000 Turks were killed, 8,000 taken prisoner (including Ali Pasha's two sons) and an unknown number drowned. On the Christian side, the casualties, including those wounded, were about 15,000 officers and men, with twelve galleys sunk and one captured. Not a single crucifix in the whole fleet was hit; but the Green Standard of Mohammed was captured – the first time in history it had ever fallen into Christian hands.†

In Constantinople, devout Moslems declared that when the Prophet heard the guns of Don John he wept upon the knees of his houris in Paradise.

'Your Majesty,' ran Don John's dispatch to Philip, 'ought to give and cause to be given, in all parts, infinite thanks to Our Lord for the great and signal victory He has been pleased to vouchsafe to this fleet and that Your Majesty may understand all that has passed, besides the report I send also Don Lope de Figueroa who can relate all the particulars Your Majesty may care to ask.

'I desire now to follow up the good fortune God has given us for the advantage of Your Majesty, and to see whether

* Another reminder in the Church of the twentieth century of this great event of the sixteenth is that the white cassock worn by the Popes of today is a reminiscence of St. Pius V's Dominican habit. It is, however, impossible to recapture emotionally what Sir Charles Petrie has so well defined: 'It lifted the pall of terror which had shrouded central and eastern Europe ever since the fall of Constantinople in 1453, and it blazoned throughout Christendom the startling fact that the Turk was no longer invincible.'

† The crucifix on Don John's flagship is now in Barcelona Cathedral; the Green Standard was preserved in the Escorial until 1671 when it perished in a fire there.

Lepanto can be taken, for that gulf is a place of great importance; and if not, what other enterprise may be attempted. Tomorrow night or the next night, we may, please God, be free to sail. Of all that happens, Your Majesty shall be informed, point by point, but that the good news may be no longer delayed I send Don Lope now, merely reminding Your Majesty of the opportunity God has placed within our reach with no greater difficulty than at once setting about providing men and galleons (of which there is no lack), money and munitions for next spring.

'I am, thank God, well, the cut on the ankle being a mere nothing. God keep and prosper Your Majesty with all the things I would wish you and of which we all stand in need.'

Philip replied: 'By the letter which came the day before yesterday by the hand of Don Lope de Figueroa, I have been pleased to a degree which it is impossible to exaggerate and not less by the particulars I have learned of the great courage and conduct you showed in the battle, by planning and ordering it all in person, as was fitting for so important an affair, and by distinguishing yourself as well as by directing others, which have without a doubt been a chief cause of this victory. And so to you, after God, ought to be given, as I now give, the honour and thanks for it.

'And some thanks are also due to me, because by a person so near and dear to me, this great business has been accomplished, and so much honour and glory, in the sight of God and the world, gained for the good of Christendom and the hurt of its enemies.' He signed it:

'Your brother,
I the King.'

The characters of the brothers ensured that, from this moment, events carried them to disaster. In any case, Philip's combination of procrastination and parsimony, which had gained him the sobriquet of 'the Prudent', were bound to exasperate Don John's insistence on immediate action. The twenty years between them were now at their most divisive. In the year of Lepanto, Philip was forty-five and prone to attacks of diarrhoea under the stress of the least anxiety; his brother was twenty-five, supremely and justifiably self-reliant as the foremost leader of men in the West, asking for men and money to consolidate his victory without delay.

And although the King, in his congratulatory letter, had the grace to admit the simple truth that in planning and ordering the campaign in person Don John was the chief cause of the victory and, after God, deserved thanks for it, he continued to treat his brother as a rash, irresponsible youth who must be subject to the advice of Royal nominees. When Philip created his favourite Requesens Viceroy of Milan as a reward for his part in Lepanto, he did not even consult Don John as to who should succeed him, so that Don John, when asked who was to occupy the vacant position, had to write: 'There are, I believe, many candidates, but I do not think it becoming to ask, having no object in thought or action beyond His Majesty's pleasure; and so I wait, in this as in other matters, to obey his orders.'

There was yet another cause of dissension. It was generally conceded by Christian leaders, from the Pope downwards, that Don John should be given a rule of his own. The territory suggested was Albania, Corfu and the Morea. It seemed that if the victor of Lepanto would carve himself a kingdom in that part of the world which had witnessed his triumph, the entire Christian population would flock to his standard and make again of Greece a power to equal any in Europe.

When, however, it was suggested to Philip that such a move would ensure a strong Spanish power at both ends of the Mediterranean the King replied that Venice, because of her possession of Cyprus and Crete, considered the Levant her sphere of influence, and that it would be diplomatically wise to do nothing at the moment. Philip, none the less, ordered his brother to keep negotiations open. Unfortunately he also became convinced that Don John was ambitious to become an independent ruler who might menace his own power. He also discovered that de Soto, who had been so carefully appointed John's secretary for the sole purpose of turning him in the right direction, had so far fallen under his young master's spell as to have taken a leading part in trying to procure him the new kingdom. When de Soto visited Madrid on Don John's behalf to inform Philip of the offer, he added a plea of his own that his master should be helped to a position for which his virtues and talents so eminently suited him! Philip controlled his anger, but did not allow the Secretary to return to the paragon; he removed him by the time-honoured device of promotion: Juan de Soto was appointed Commissary-General of the Spanish Navy.

The Pope had another possible plan for a kingdom for Don John which had preceded Lepanto. When, in 1570, he had excommunicated Elizabeth of England, he had thought of Don John as a suitable consort for Mary Queen of Scots, the rightful Queen of England, imprisoned by the usurping heretic. For the moment nothing could be done because Mary's third husband, the Earl of Bothwell, who had abducted and then deserted her, was still alive and though the nullity of that marriage was obvious enough, it had to be established by the due processes of law which would entail a measure of unwelcome publicity.

In the months that followed Lepanto, Pius V was indefatigable in trying to secure the support of other Christian rulers for the Holy League. He sent his legates to the Kings of France, Poland and Portugal and to the Emperor urging them to take arms against the infidel; but the Emperor refused to break his treaty of neutrality with the Turks, the King of Poland was fully occupied in defending his country against the attacks of the Tsar of Russia, Ivan the Terrible, and France was bedevilled with the rebellion of the Huguenots. Only the seventeen-year-old Sebastian of

Portugal, nephew of Philip and Don John, promised help – at least to the extent of keeping his coasts clear of Barbary Corsairs.

That year, 1572, Easter fell on 6 April and the Pope, though feeling unwell, was able to give his usual blessing from the balcony of St. Peter's *urbi et orbi*. In spite of the remonstrances of his doctors, he subsequently insisted on doing the pilgrimage of the Seven Churches, partly in a litter, partly on foot. The Abbot of St. Paul's-without-the Walls and his Benedictines assured him of their prayers for his renewed health.

'No, my sons,' he said. 'I am laying down the burden. Pray that I may have a good successor. At this moment it is important to Christianity.' And when, on 1 May, Pius V laid his burden down, his last thoughts were of the Holy League: 'It may not be easy to find one who has a stronger desire to root out the enemies of Christ's faith and cross. But by the blood of Christ I entreat you, whose affair it is, to elect as quickly as possible a zealous man in my place and not to choose him on mere worldly considerations. The Holy League has begun a great work, but the year is already advanced and what has to be done must be done soon for if this year passes without some memorable action, men's spirits will fail them and our labour and the great victory will be fruitless.'

The saint's last words were: 'Defend me from the enemy and receive me in the hour of death.'

Don John, meanwhile, was at Messina with the fleet ready to sail. Philip would not give the order. The new Pope, Gregory XIII, did his best to fulfil his predecessor's wishes and in June sent a message to remind Philip that the proceeds of the bull of the crusade and other ecclesiastical revenues had been granted to him to assist his preparations against the Sultan and that if he did not take the offensive quickly, these concessions could not be continued.

Philip took no notice. The Turkish commander took to

sea again, with the message: 'You should understand the differences between your loss and ours. In taking Cyprus from you, we have deprived you of an arm. In defeating our fleet, you have only shaved our beard. An arm when cut off cannot grow again, but a beard grows better for the razor.'

Almost in desperation, Don John wrote a long letter to his brother warning him that this continued delay was endangering the very existence of the Holy League and imploring him either to allow him to sail or, at the very least, to send a portion of his fleet to support the Venetians whose territory was again being attacked by the Turks.

Philip took a month to reply, but eventually gave his permission and on 8 September – Our Lady's Birthday – Don John was able once more to lead the fleet of the Holy League into the Mediterranean to try to bring the Mohammedans to battle. But it was too late in the season. Apart from one or two skirmishes, in which the Christians had the advantage, there was no engagement and on 25 October Don John had to start to distribute his troops in their winter quarters. He was too furious to hide his dissatisfaction with Philip's policy and angrily waved aside the compliment that the Turkish commander's refusal to meet him was, in itself, the greatest of tributes that could be paid to his reputation.

The King, on his side, was consumed with anger – and suspicion – when he heard that the new Pope had said in full consistory: 'That young commander has proved himself a Scipio in valour, a Pompey in heroic grace, an Augustus in good fortune; a new Moses, a new Gideon, a new Samson, a new Saul, a new David, without the faults of those famous men; and I hope to God to live long enough to reward him with a royal crown.'

Once more Philip urgently sought the advice of Ruy Gómez.

VI
A Change of Secretaries

Ruy was at Pastrana with Ana and their children and Escovedo, as his secretary, enjoying the peace of home life on his beloved estate. Much of his time he spent with Teresa's friars in the little house he had given, for, though Father Mariano had renounced the world and embraced holy solitude, that hermit-friar felt too beholden to the Prince for his generosity to erect against him a barrier of professional silence. Also, they had known each other well at Court.

Mariano Azaro, a Neapolitan, was a Knight of the Order of St. John of Jerusalem and, for a period, Master of the Palace to the Queen of Poland. He was also a great geometer, a skilled mathematician and one of the best engineers of the day. He had fought at the battle of St. Quentin and later King Philip had employed him on constructing a canal connecting the Tagus with the Guadalquivir. He had a notable aversion to women and, though he naturally had the courtesy to attempt to hide from Ruy his opinion of Ana, Ruy was not unaware of it and occasionally, now that Mariano had fallen under the influence of Mother Teresa, gently rallied him on his exemplary service of and obedience to a woman. But as a rule they spoke of spiritual and religious matters. Ruy, though still in his early fifties, had recently had some twinges of illness and was concerned to 'make his soul' should death unexpectedly call him; and Mariano, in Teresa's words, 'had long ago received grace from Our Lord to realise the nature of the world and to strive to withdraw from it'. But, even when immersed in it, he had on one particular occasion taken a course of action which had fascinated Ruy Gómez.

Mariano had been accused some years previously of being implicated in a political murder and had, on that account, spent two years in prison. He had refused to engage any advocate or anyone else to defend him on the grounds that, as he was innocent, he could safely depend on the justice of God. All he asked was the right to question the witnesses against him. There were three, each of whom swore that Mariano had approached him to commit the murder. Mariano, remembering the tactics of Daniel in the Biblical story of Susanna, saw to it that each was asked separately where he, Mariano, was at the time. One replied that he was sitting on a bed and another that he was standing at a window. In the end they had to confess that they had invented the story. Having thus vindicated God's judgment, Mariano demonstrated further the nature of human justice by using much of his fortune in bribing the authorities not to proceed against the perjurers, thus also incidentally demonstrating the Christian precept: 'Bless them that persecute you and do good to those that despitefully use you.'

Such a course of action was frankly unintelligible to Ruy who had imbibed from his boyhood the precepts of high diplomacy which regarded magnanimity as a risky card and one to be played very sparingly. At the moment, however, he was feeling at peace with the world – and therefore more inclined to take an objective view of things – because he had at last won his life-long duel with Alba.

The Duke's position as Governor of the Netherlands was best expressed in a confidential letter the unhappy warrior had written to his friend, Zayas, one of Philip's Secretaries, in which he roundly accused the King of ingratitude. His Majesty, said Alba, treated him 'like a dead man'. He had been in the Low Countries for six years, perishing from hunger and fatigue; he had spent three hundred thousand crowns of his own money, and no longer had enough to live on. His plight ought to move 'even a Prince different from ours, whom we have seen grant great favours to those who have served him well'.

Philip not only ignored the hint but actually wrote to Requesens, who was enjoying himself as Governor of Milan, saying that he was concerned about the state of the Netherlands and offering the Governorship of them to 'the prudent, diligent and careful' Requesens himself. Eventually Alba had been recalled and Requesens sent to Brussels in his place.

These events, gratifying as they were, Ruy did not discuss with Father Mariano who, even as a layman, had showed no particular interest in court intrigues at any level. When they spoke at all of people as distinct from principles, the friar seemed interested in one only – the unfortunate Don Carlos. It so happened that Louis de Foix, the famous French architect who had been responsible for much of the design of the Escorial, had been professionally acquainted with Mariano. They had both specialised in the machinery required for the irrigation of heights and Mariano had actually used a modification of the method by which de Foix had carried the water of the Tagus to the highest points of Toledo to bring water to the top of the hill at Pastrana and so to irrigate the little kitchen-gardens and orchards of the friars' hermitages.

One day while this operation was in progress Mariano asked Ruy whether he remembered a day in the spring of 1568 – four years ago – when King Philip had visited his palace of Aranjuez.

'Why should I remember it particularly? His Majesty often goes to hear the song of the nightingales in the gardens of Aranjuez. It is more beautiful there than anywhere else in the world!'

'I know,' said Mariano, 'and His Majesty is not wrong. The Aranjuez nightingales, like the gardens, are *non pareil*.'

'But why the particular occasion?' asked Ruy, warily.

'Would you understand me if I said that it was because you were not accompanying him?'

Ruy remembered and understood perfectly. It was the only day in the not-to-be-remembered thirty weeks between Don Carlos's arrest and his death on which the King consented to leave the Madrid palace where both were imprisoned. The strain of those weeks had become so intolerable that Ruy had feared that Philip would break under it. Suggestion after suggestion had been made for some visit to relieve the voluntary gaolership but not even the Escorial could tempt the King from Madrid. Then, suddenly, the week after his birthday, Philip decided to go to Aranjuez to give his decision on a detail of the irrigation of the palace gardens from the Tagus which Louis de Foix was carrying out for him.

Ruy had not accompanied him because Ruy was the one person he could totally trust to see that nothing went wrong in his absence. Ruy also needed no explanation for the journey. He, most intimate of friends, knew what Aranjuez signified to Philip – all the happiness of his boyhood with his mother and sisters, and the beginning of love with the exquisite fifteen-year-old Princess who died giving birth to Don Carlos. The visit to Aranjuez in the May of his forty-first birthday was to be interpreted as a desperate attempt to call in the past to right the balance of the present and to exorcise the murderous mutual hatred between him and his only son by the memory of himself as a sixteen-year-old father rejoicing in his heir and moved to incomprehensible tears by the singing of the nightingales in the three-mile-long avenue of elms which he had dedicated to his child-wife.

'Had you anything in mind about that particular occasion?' Ruy asked Mariano.

The slight acerbity of tone warned the friar that this was not the time for full confidences. 'No,' he said, 'except that the matter on which His Majesty consulted de Foix and me seemed too trivial for such an expedition. It would have been enough to have studied the model.'

'You will remember de Foix was returning to Paris. His Majesty may have wished to know that you were in complete agreement, in case he did not return.'

'Certainly we understood each other better after the visit.'

There, for the moment, they allowed the matter to rest.

In fact, Mariano's professional relationship with de Foix had after that day become a personal friendship in the course of which the affairs of Court had been discussed in a light which increased the Neapolitan's determination to become a religious. He was, in the absence of any proof to the contrary, prepared to believe the stories that the King had murdered his son, for de Foix had told him how he had arranged for Don Carlos who always wished to be alone at night without any servant to wait on him, a set of pulleys by means of which he could open or shut his door without rising from his bed. On the Christmas Eve of 1567, de Foix had been urgently summoned by the King and ordered to alter the pulleys in such a manner that the door could be opened without the usual noise which was almost certain to awaken Don Carlos were he asleep. Because of the alteration, it had been possible for the King, with Ruy Gómez and the others, to enter the room without waking the Infante and to disarm him before he was fully awake of the pistols he kept under his pillows and the sword which hung on the bed-post.

From that day no one other than his guards had seen Don Carlos and when his death was announced – the news of it coincided with that of Alba's victory over the Dutch rebels at Jemmingen – Mariano, at least, was inclined to believe the gossip which suggested that the prince had had poison put into his broth and his corpse preserved on ice until such time as was most propitious to announce the death.

Ruy Gómez by implication had denied this by talking much of the great blocks of ice which Don Carlos had had put into his bed in a mad attempt to kill himself with cold, but, though Mariano was tact itself in discussing this strange vagary of the Infante's, its only effect was to turn his suspicions to virtual certainty.

The matter of Don Carlos came into the two men's conversation once more as Ruy prepared to leave Pastrana to advise Philip about Don John. As Ruy was himself intending to retire completely from Court by the end of 1573 and devote himself in what he called his old age to Ana and their ten children, he had already allowed Antonio Pérez to enter directly the King's service with a view to replacing him as principal Secretary and had kept for himself only Juan de Escovedo. Should he now let Escovedo go to Don John, as he had once seconded de Soto?

'Can you spare him?' asked Mariano. .

'If it is best for the King's service that I should.'

'You care for him greatly?'

'Who? The King or Escovedo?'

'I mean, of course, Escovedo. All the world knows your love for Philip.'

'Both Escovedo and Pérez have become like sons to me. I have let the one go to Philip, so why should I not give the other to Don John? After all, I am retiring from affairs. What do I need but Ana and the children in the peace of Pastrana?'

'Then,' said the hermit, 'let him go to Don John and pray for his safety.'

More than this, in spite of Ruy's further attempts to reach his mind, Mariano would not say.

A few weeks later, on 29 July 1573, in the stifling heat of a Madrid summer, Ruy Gómez, Duke of Pastrana, Prince of Eboli, collapsed and died, leaving King Philip without any adviser he could unreservedly trust.

VII

Sister Ana of the Mother of God

At her husband's death, the Princess of Eboli was prostrated with an hysterical grief of an intensity equal to if not indeed greater than that which had afflicted her aunt, Doña Luisa, on her widowing and which had resulted in bringing Teresa of Avila into the orbit of the Mendozas. Not that Ana had any desire to see Teresa. She found the nun so *non simpatico* that there would be no consolation in hearing her assurances of Heaven. And how could one who had renounced marriage understand the loss of a husband, especially a husband like Ruy? He had filled Ana's horizon since she was a girl of twelve and in the fifteen years of their actual marriage he had given her ten children, each one a pledge of love. Now the only landmark left was, oddly enough, the convent at Pastrana. While Ruy's body was lying in state, Ana busied herself in making with her own hands a Carmelite habit and, on the day of his burial, she ordered the chaplain to clothe her with it and give her the name in religion of Sister Ana of the Mother of God. It was a dramatic enough gesture but at that moment it had the redeeming sincerity of utter despair. She would remain with her husband in a kind of death in their convent in their loved Pastrana. She was certain that Ruy would have approved and as soon as the funeral was over she set off for Pastrana in an old, completely closed cart in imitation of Mother Teresa.

The prioress, the 25-year-old Isabel of St. Dominic, when she received the news, exclaimed: 'The Princess a nun! That will be the end of this house!' Teresa herself was equally apprehensive, foreseeing the inevitable clash of wills which led to the catastrophe she later chronicled thus: 'The convent was most highly favoured by the Prince and Princess of Eboli, the latter being most careful to look after them and treat them well until the death of Prince Ruy Gómez. Then, either through the wiles of the devil or perhaps because the Lord allowed it, the Princess, overcome with grief at his death, entered the convent as a nun herself. In the state of distress she was in, the restrictions imposed by the enclosure, to which she was not accustomed, could not have pleased her and, on account of the Holy Council*, the Prioress could not give her all the freedom she desired.'

Father Francisco de Santamaria thus described the arrival of the Princess. 'The Prioress called the nuns, got ready the house, and prepared two beds, one for the Princess, the other for her mother. The Princess changed her habit, as the one she had taken in Madrid was neither suitable nor so clean as it might have been. She rested for a while, and suddenly showing her determination wished that the habit should be given at once to the two waiting-maids she had brought with her, paying with a little sackcloth the salaries of long years. The Prioress answered that the licence of the prelate was necessary. She said, very much offended, 'what have friars to do with my convent?'. Not without resentment on the Princess's part, the Mother Prioress deferred doing it until she had consulted the Father Prior. Having conferred with him she resolved to give them the habit. This was done in the parlour, the Princess being placed between the two, so that she might also attain the blessings. They took her to eat meat with her mother in a room apart. She dispensed with this service and went to the refectory, and leaving the place near the Prioress which had been

* The Council of Trent, which reformed the laxity into which so many religious houses had fallen. The second Vatican Council has recently restored the laxity.

prepared for her took one of the lowest, without giving in to prayers and exhortations, preserving superiority in an inferior place.

'The Prioress, considering that such self-will would cause much trouble, thought that it would be better if the lady took a part of the house, where she could live with her servants and be visited by secular people, with a door to go to the cloister when she wished, but not any secular person to use it. This seemed to everyone good advice, but she thought it bad, as it was not hers, and she remained as she was in the convent.

'The next day, having buried the Prince and performed the obsequies, the Bishop of Segorbe and other persons of rank who were there came to visit her. Mother Elizabeth told her to talk to them at the grating, but she wished that they should come into the cloister, and made such a point of this that, in spite of the monks, nuns, and laymen who came to visit her, they opened the doors of the convent and many servants entered with the lords, overthrowing the decrees of the Council, the orders of the holy Mother, the silence and retirement of the nuns and all good government, because lords do not think they need obey laws. Not content with this she insisted on having two secular maids; the Mother Prioress offered that she herself and everyone would wait on her, especially two novices formerly in her service, but nothing would satisfy her, as she thought that she should be obeyed.

'The Mother Elizabeth wrote to our Mother St. Teresa, telling her of the death of the Prince, the resolution of the Princess, and the first episodes she had gone through with her.

'Mother Elizabeth and two of her oldest nuns told her that if she went on in this way, they knew that the holy foundation would take them away and put them where they could keep their rules, of more importance in her eyes than all the Grandees in the world. Annoyed by this, she took her servants and went to a hermitage in the orchard, and remained there, having nothing to do with the nuns. They sent her, however, the novices to wait on her, they not being yet so bound by the rules of the cloister.

'From there a door opened into the street, by which she admitted everyone, modifying thereby the grief for her husband's death. Because of all this the work of the church and convent stopped and the alms which Ruy Gómez had left for its support, so that it began to suffer great straits.'

It was not long before the scandal grew to such proportions that the Prioress courteously but firmly told her that it was too great an honour for a poor convent to have her among them and that only the Court was worthy of her. Ana did not mistake her meaning and protested that she was being turned out. Angrily she wrote to the King, but Philip told her bluntly that her first duty was to look after her children.

So she returned to her own house in Pastrana to amuse herself by harassing the nuns. Her first step was to withdraw the revenue she had undertaken to give them when the house had been founded, which was tantamount to imposing near-starvation, since there was no help to be had in so isolated a spot. The next move was a suggestion of theft, but here the Prioress proved a match for the Princess. She had made a note of everything Ana had given to the convent, both in the way of ordinary things and of sacred vessels or vestments. She then sent for the *Corregidor* and a notary public and, inventory in hand, gave back to the Princess everything which did not form a part of the convent's original possession.

Teresa, meanwhile, determined to move the Pastrana nuns to the new house she had founded at Segovia. She enlisted the help of two devoted friends, her chaplain and fellow-townsman, Julián of Avila, and Antonio Gaytán, a widower of some means who had developed such a zeal for the reformed Carmelites that he begged Teresa to make use of him for whatever the Order needed. Gaytán now hired five carts, which they considered would be ample accommodation for the fourteen Pastrana nuns and their possessions, and on the evening of Palm Sunday, 3 April 1574, set off from Segovia for Pastrana. They halted at some distance from the village in order not to arouse curiosity. The two rescuers went on, conquering their fear, until they reached the walls of the convent which they scaled without too much difficulty. They made their way to the chapel where their first action was to consume the Reserved Sacrament in the tabernacle; then, fortified by 'the Bread of the strong', the nuns followed their rescuers in single file on tiptoe. The silence of that hour before dawn seemed to suggest the silence of an ambush and Julián de Avila, who frankly admitted his constitutional timidity, said afterwards that to escape in the way and at the time they were doing took more courage than would have been required by a frontal attack in daylight.

At last they arrived safely where the carts were awaiting them and amid the clatter of galloping mules, cracking of whips and shouts of the muleteers the last stage of the escape began. Apart from being nearly drowned crossing the Jarama (which Julián de Avila compared to the sea) the fugitives encountered no danger and, on reaching Segovia, were installed in the new convent there by Mother Teresa who appointed as Prioress Sister Isabel of St. Dominic as some recognition of the proof she had given of her wisdom, courage and wit in her dealings with Sister Ana of the Mother of God.

Ana's first instinct, when her steward brought her news of the nuns' escape, was to order him to collect a sufficient force to ride after them and bring them back. But almost immediately she realised that she did not want them back. What good were they or their convent to her now? At the crisis of her life they had failed her. To have them now would be to intensify the bitterness. So she let them go and kept the reprisal she planned for Mother Teresa alone. She would strike her down in her own time.

When Ana, staying at her aunt's palace, had first met the holy nun from Avila, Teresa, under obedience to her confessor, was writing her autobiography. The work was naturally discussed in the household and eventually a copy was made for Doña Luisa. Unfortunately this did not remain the only copy. Ana prevailed on her aunt to let her have yet another made. Though Teresa had protested, Ana had promised that the manuscript should be read by no one but Ruy and herself. But now she made it accessible to anybody who cared to read it. Its contents began to be widely known and its most intimate spiritual revelations to be laughed at or dismissed as fraud or delusion. Particular amusement was derived from Teresa's visions which were laughingly compared with the deceits twenty years earlier of Magdalena de la Cruz, a Poor Clare whose credit for prophecy and reputation for holiness were such that attempts were made to canonise her in her lifetime, but who eventually publicly confessed that her holiness was simulated, her ecstasies feigned and her wonder-working the result of a pact with the Devil. The Holy Office had taken the matter up and the story had profoundly shocked all Spain. It also unleashed a flood, so it seemed, of false mystics, of claimants to the stigmata, of *alumbrados, illuminées* following their own 'inner light', of hysterics indulging in sham ecstasies and claiming extraordinary raptures.

Once the Inquisition took measures to restore orthodoxy, the position became more equivocal and complicated. Every effect of the love of God perceptible to the senses became suspect. Where once people thought they had seen God, they now imagined they saw Satan. And, though there was a danger of external manifestations being judged a mere pretence, the abandonment of them was no less dangerous. To remain kneeling during the Gospel, to fix one's eyes on the ground during the Elevation of the Host, not to fast or mortify oneself was to invite the interest of the Holy Office and since, as one result of the Council of Trent, there was a tendency to class any subtle deviation from simple orthodoxy as 'Lutheranism', there was the danger of death where once there had been the likelihood of a mere reprimand for ignorant excursions into the minutiae of theology. Any work of spirituality written in Spanish, with very few exceptions, was immediately placed on the Index.

It was, in fact, to protect Teresa, as a genuine mystic, from official misunderstandings that her confessors had insisted that she write her autobiography. Taken as a whole and allowance being made for the patent goodness and good faith of the writer, no instructed theologian of the Holy Office could suspect heresy.

But its effect on uninstructed laity, prompted by malice, was very different. The spite and ridicule of the household of the Princess of Eboli was echoed that summer in Madrid and one of the Court's greatest amusements was to introduce, in order to hear Ana's comments, Mother Teresa's account of one of her visions: 'On the Festival of the Assumption of Our Lady thinking of the many sins which in times past I had confessed in that monastery and of other things concerning my wicked life, there came upon me a rapture so vehement that it nearly drew me out of myself altogether. I sat down and even now I remember that I could neither see the Elevation nor hear Mass being said, and later this caused a certain amount of scruple.

'While in this state, I thought I saw myself being clothed in a garment of great whiteness and brightness. At first I could not see who was clothing me, but later I saw Our Lady on my right hand, my father Saint Joseph on my left and it was they who were putting the garment on me. I was given to understand I was now cleansed of my sins.

'When the clothing was ended and I was experiencing the greatest joy and bliss, I thought that Our Lady suddenly took me by the hands and told me I was giving her great pleasure by serving the glorious Saint Joseph and that all I was trying to do about the convent would be accomplished and that both Our Lord and they two would be greatly served in it. They would keep us safe and her Son had already promised to go with us; as a sign that that was true, she said, she would give me this jewel. Then she seemed to throw round my neck a very beautiful gold collar to which was fastened a most valuable cross. The gold and stones were so different from earthly things of the kind that no comparison between them is possible. Their beauty is quite unlike anything we can imagine, and the understanding cannot soar high enough to comprehend the nature of the garment or to imagine the brightness of the vision which it was the Lord's will to send me and by comparison with which everything on earth looks, one might say, like a smudge of soot.'

When the greatest amount of amusement had been extracted from this and similar episodes and when extensive gossip had already aroused the interest of the Grand Inquisitor, the Princess of Eboli officially sent a copy of the *Life* to the Holy Office, denouncing it as a book containing 'visions, revelations and the setting forth of dangerous doctrine'.

VIII
A Kingdom for Don John?

The death of Ruy Gómez was tragic enough for Ana, but for the King it was little less than catastrophic. The personal loss to Philip of the intimate friend of a lifetime was also the political loss to the monarch of the only man in Spain worthy of the name of statesman among the aristocrats and ecclesiastics bent on safeguarding and extending the privileges of their own orders and the new men determined to impress their names on posterity. The loss was intensified by the fact that Ruy, the great reconciler of the royal brothers, had, so to speak, left his spirit split between them. The two men he had trained, Pérez and Escovedo, promoted the incipient rivalry; for Escovedo fell under the spell of Don John's legendary ability and charm even more completely than had de Soto, while Pérez, determined to become Philip's *éminence grise* to an extent to which Ruy Gómez had never dreamt of aspiring, darkened every suspicion and exaggerated every grievance which Philip entertained of Don John's ambition. Things had, indeed, reached a crisis in the relationship between the brothers that no one but Ruy himself could have averted.

Don John was now twenty-seven and was quite aware that few men in the world's history had risen so high at so comparatively early an age; nor had the offer of the throne of Greece been forgotten, even though it had not been accepted. In addition, there was a general consensus of opinion, outside the Spanish court, that he should be made an independent ruler. St. Pius V, before he died, had written to Philip suggesting a marriage between Don John and Mary Queen of Scots (with the approval of Mary's uncle, the Duke of Lorraine), which would have made him King of Scotland *de facto* as well as – because Elizabeth was excommunicate – King of England *de jure*. Philip showed no enthusiasm for the project.

In the October of 1573, three months after Ruy Gómez's death, Don John captured Tunis from the Turks and at the beginning of 1574 Escovedo went to Rome on a secret mission to St. Pius V's successor, Gregory XIII, to ask him to intercede with King Philip to allow Don John to assume the crown of Tunis.

Consequently, on 16 January 1574, the Papal Nuncio in Spain presented King Philip with a memorandum saying that His Holiness had heard with great concern and some alarm that the Spanish fleet was about to be reduced and Don John recalled from the command of it. In view of the continued Turkish threat to Christendom he doubted the prudence of both steps. Surely the fleet should be increased rather than diminished and Don John encouraged to take the offensive while 'it might be well to consider whether it would not add to his power and authority were he invested with the title of King of Tunis, so that Your Majesty might show your gratitude for the conquest, after the manner of your ancestors, by founding a new Christian kingdom'.

As an alternative the Pope suggested that it might even be advantageous if Don John 'were to undertake the enterprise of England it being much desired as it has already been clearly shown by English Catholics that he should become their King by marriage with Mary Queen of Scots'.

Philip, masking his irritation, replied after a suitable delay that the Pope might rest assured that he need not concern himself lest Don John's services should go unrewarded for his advancement was very close to the King's heart, but that the rewards proposed were neither adequate for those services nor as yet sufficiently in his power to grant, but that the matter would certainly, at a fitting opportunity, receive the careful consideration it deserved.

In the spring of the following year, 1575, the Pope made another attempt to gain Philip's interest in the matter of England. This time Philip, after three months' delay, played it differently. He sent to Rome an Irish friar, Patrick O'Healey, in an attempt to gain the Pope's blessing on a certain Irish gentleman, whose name he did not disclose, to raise a revolt against Queen Elizabeth. He said that if the Irish Catholics could be assured that their leader was acting with the authority of the Holy Father they would in a few days overthrow English rule in Ireland and then gladly accept Don John for their monarch. The friar assured the Pope that he had discussed the matter with the King of Spain and that Philip had given it his blessing.

The matter was put into the hands of the Cardinal responsible for Ireland with the result that the Spanish Ambassador wrote to Philip approving of the scheme in general but suggesting that the name of Don John should be omitted because he had noticed that whenever the Pope discussed English politics he stressed that no French or Spanish claimant to the Crown must be put forward but that the candidature of some native English or Scottish must be supported. This, the Ambassador affected to think, was because 'he was very much resolved that Your Majesty should not acquire more territory than you now have; and it might be if Don John were to obtain the Kingdom of Ireland, His Holiness would think it as much the property of Your Majesty as any of the realms God has already given you'.

Though the King received this letter on 14 July, he did not trouble to reply to it till 8 September. He then pointed out that he had done no more than give Father O'Healey a letter of introduction and that the friar had no authority whatever to enter into discussion of any political topic. He also drew attention to the fact that the Pope's reputed opposition to

Don John's candidature for a throne was in direct contradiction to his attitude the previous March. Nevertheless, he was prepared to guarantee the pay of two thousand mercenaries for six months, as well as defraying the cost of their transport to England, on condition that the enterprise was conducted wholly in the Pope's name and the strictest secrecy was observed.

The Pope's reply was uncooperative. In the long delay some of his enthusiasm had evaporated. He was quite willing that the expedition should sail from Civita Vecchia under the Papal flag and be commanded by one of whom Philip approved, but considering that the King would reap all the benefit of success it was only equitable that he should bear the entire cost of the enterprise, which he put at a hundred thousand crowns. It was, of course, impossible for the Holy See to hold any territory in the British Isles, but some compensation in Italy would not come amiss. The ambassador privately excused himself to the King for allowing himself to treat this matter as practical politics, explaining that unless some such hope were encouraged in Gregory there was little hope of help from him.

Meanwhile an Independent adventurer, Thomas Stucley, who was *au fait* with the Irish situation visited Naples and had an interview with Don John, who duly reported it to Philip with the comment, 'I ended our long conversation by telling Stucley he ought to go back to Rome and continue the negotiation, I having made him promise and having promised on my own part to keep the matter secret, which is of equal importance to the affair and to his own personal safety. I humbly beg that Your Majesty will order due consideration to be given as to what ought to be done in this business for your service. To me it appears that if the Pope resolves to take up the enterprise and defray the cost of it, it will open a way by which the affairs of Flanders may be helped, and Your Majesty may be considerably served.'

After an even more lengthy delay than usual, Philip sent a

noncommittal reply, telling his brother that he had done well to inform him of the interview, though he must be careful not to encourage such overtures. All the same it was just as well to hear anything the English Catholic exiles had to say.

Meanwhile, in North Africa, the fruits of Don John's great victory over the Turks in the capture of Tunis had been lost. Philip's original instructions had been to dismantle the place, but Don John had persuaded him to allow the building of a fort, La Goletta, to defend it and to develop it as a Christian territory under a Mohammedan viceroy. But once again the royal parsimony and delay had brought the great plan to nothing. Within a year Tunis and the Goletta were re-taken by the Turks and the Spanish garrison killed. The King's letter, containing the usual pedantic instructions, marked a crisis in the relationship between the brothers.

'Your Majesty does me great honour', wrote Don John in reply, 'in stating the reasons for which you forbid me to go in person against the enemy. I must nevertheless take leave to point out that, knowing what the safety of this fleet requires, no personal object or interest shall ever prevent me undertaking what I consider most advantageous for your service; and I therefore once more entreat Your Majesty to be pleased sometimes to refer such questions as these to us who are on the spot where they arise.'

He also announced his intention of visiting Madrid immediately as the only way of preventing further disaster 'the difficulties of the business being so many and the distance between Italy and Madrid so great, that time, however precious, is always being wasted'.

Philip replied with unaccustomed promptitude, forbidding him to visit Spain. 'Although I should be exceedingly glad to see you here, I have determined to postpone my private gratification to the benefit and security of public affairs; and you must be contented to do the same.'

At the same time the Pope, who kept an extremely informed eye on Spanish policy, wrote to Philip: 'These unhappy events in Africa have filled us with grief and confusion. Never could we have believed Your Majesty's Ministers would have been so negligent in not giving aid of all kinds to these poor people. We do not blame one more than another, but we do say in general that Your Majesty is very badly served and that if you do not soon provide a remedy which can be seen and understood by all we fear that, old as we are*, we shall ourselves witness the ruin of Christendom – which God forbid.'

Don John, preferring 'the guilt of disobedience to the certainty of dishonour', made the journey from Italy to Spain despite his brother's prohibition. He arrived in Catalonia on 30 December 1574, and wrote at once to Antonio Pérez saying that it no doubt appeared strange that he had acted in violation of Philip's instructions, 'Yet God is my witness that I believe and know that what I do is what ought to be done and that up to this time no one at Court has troubled to understand how dangerous is the state of His Majesty's affairs in Italy and how entirely the treatment of them must be changed if it is ever to be better. I may add that in order not to see myself a minister of mischief from which there is no honourable escape – mischief long foreseen and denounced – I have left my post and incurred the guilt of disobedience rather than the certainty of dishonour. Now I am anxious to know what kind of welcome I have to expect; for welcome I do not look for, however my zeal may have deserved it.'

Ruy Gómez was less than eighteen months dead, yet it might have been another century and a new revolutionary regime. Ever since, as an amazed boy, Don John had first been brought to Court, Ruy had been there to appeal to for understanding and guidance or to mediate between the incompatible brothers. But now access to the King was by way of the inconsiderable figure of Ruy's secretary, Antonio Pérez, who, with limitless ambition, aspired to his

* Gregory was seventy-two.

master's place with the King. And, in a way – though Don John did not realise it – had attained it.

An objective observer wrote: 'Antonio Pérez, Secretary of State, is the pupil of Ruy Gómez. He is very discreet and amiable and has great knowledge and authority. By his agreeable manners he tempers and disguises much of the disgust which people would feel at the King's slowness and sordid parsimony. Through his hands have passed all the affairs of Italy and also those of Flanders. He is so clever and capable that he will obviously become the King's principal adviser. He is thin, of delicate health and fond of his advantages and pleasures. He loves being flattered and receiving presents and bribes.'

Gradually, exercising his immense charm and tact, Pérez gained control of the King to an extent of which Philip himself was quite unaware. There were some who thought his power greater than even Ruy Gómez's had been.

On this occasion, Pérez was sufficiently flattered by Don John's attitude to him as a powerful intermediary to urge the King to receive his brother amicably and in the early days of March the two sons of the great Emperor Charles V met face to face in the new palace in Madrid to discuss the intolerable burden of rule which their father had left them. Spain and the Indies, Africa and the Netherlands posed problems which only a strong united government could solve. Don John, proud in his fidelity to his royal brother, requested the title of Infante of Spain*; Philip, cruelly suspicious of Don John's reasons for seeking an increase of personal sphere of influence, refused to discuss it, though he did not rule out the possibility of it.

When he left the King Don John rode north to visit his beloved foster-mother, Doña Magdalena de Ulloa, who had prepared for her darling the usual extensive supply of linen made with her own hands. On the way, he decided to

* The title of Infante is normally the prerogative of legitimate children of the monarch of Spain.

see the Escorial. The morning he set out was still and bright, but before he had accomplished half the journey a storm of unusual fury broke out. The wind rose to hurricane force, with thunder, lightning and hail and the ilex-covered chase was strewn with broken boughs and upturned roots of trees, while masses of rock rattled down the sides of the misty hills.

Of Don John's attendants, some were driven to seek shelter by the unprecedented fury of the storm; others with their horses were laid prone by the wind; but Don John, excellently mounted, rode on alone and alighted at the gate of the grey palace-convent. He forbade the Prior and the monks to emerge beyond the threshold on the grounds that the weather was fit only for a soldier like himself to be out in.

The association of Don John with natural storms continued into the next year. It was almost as if men sought to connect his explosive personality with the phenomena of the Heavens. In the opening weeks of 1576 he decided to fulfil his obligation to Our Lady which he had undertaken at Lepanto – to visit the Holy House at her shrine at Loreto – which pressure of public business had hitherto prevented him fulfilling. He had, of course, obtained a dispensation to enable him to defer the visit with a good conscience: but the priority nagged at him. Now, setting out, he found the roads bad, the rivers in flood and the weather in general unpleasantly severe. It was raining heavily when he passed the port of Recanati and had his first view of the great dome which covered the Holy House. Despite the storm, he took off his hat and cloak and, so long as the church remained in sight, remained bareheaded and uncloaked 'as if ', noted an admiring chronicler, 'he desired to make an offering of himself to the Blessed Virgin to whose benignity he owed his life'. Having arrived at Loreto, he performed all the rites and ceremonies of the pilgrimage with an overwhelming devotion. It was as if he had anticipated the crisis in his life brought about by the sudden death on 5 March 1576 of the Grand Commander Requesens, Governor of the Netherlands.

IX
The New Governor

It was of the highest interest to Spain that a successor to the Grand Commander be appointed immediately and Philip established a record in his reign by deliberating for only a fortnight. In a letter of 8 April 1576, he informed Don John that he had decided to appoint him to the post. To pacify the Provinces and to safeguard religion, he wrote, the first thing was to entrust the Government to a Prince of the Blood. Don John was therefore at once to set off for Lombardy where instructions and powers would be sent to him. The King only wished that his letter had wings, so that it might fly into his brother's hands and that Don John himself had wings that he might the sooner reach Flanders.

The Prince was to travel with as small a retinue as possible – at most a dozen. No one – *no one* – except Escovedo was to be informed of the object of his journey. The fleet was to be left under the command of the Duke of Sesa, as if for a very short time; and Don John was to take no one with him from Naples except Escovedo and some personal servants – and of them as few as possible because the Netherlanders, seeing him arrive among them without troops or armour or counsellors or household, putting himself, as it were, into their power with every appearance of confidence, would receive him with the greater love and satisfaction.

This letter was delivered to Don John in Naples on 3 May by the same courier who brought no less than three letters on the same subject from Antonio Pérez to Escovedo. They were meant, obviously, for Don John's eyes. Pérez used every argument he could think of to induce the Prince to hasten to the Low Countries, reminding him of his duty to the King, the urgency of the crisis and the glory he would gain if he alone was seen to be able to pacify the Netherlands and which would eclipse even the reputation he had so rightly acquired at Lepanto. The greatest secrecy was to be observed and even the Pope was to be kept in ignorance of the appointment until Don John himself wrote him a letter announcing it to the Spanish Ambassador from the road northward. A second letter, concerned mainly with money, gave authorisation for the taking of fifteen to twenty thousand ducats from the last payment of cash made on account of the fleet.

In Pérez's third letter, a postscript was added by the King's order. Escovedo was asked, before giving the King's letter into Don John's hands, to obtain a promise that Don John would inform no one at all of its contents. Nor was Don John on any account to think of visiting Madrid.

More than anything else, perhaps, the drafts of these letters*, with their marginal notes and interpolations in the King's maddening handwriting, convinced both Escovedo and his master of Philip's almost hysterical anxiety. But anxiety for what? And what was the object of this elaborate, four-handed game? And who was formulating the rules?

Escovedo puzzled over a passage in Pérez's third letter. 'So it is, my friend, that I feel that Don John should obey His Majesty with much love and eagerness, setting off at once, imitating his father who on a like occasion ventured himself into the midst of his enemies in order to bring the single city of Ghent to reason and who by that means obtained his end. And I hope that the result of a like determination will in this case be as much the greater as the necessity is the more urgent.' At the end of the first of these sentences, the King

* They are preserved at Simancas.

had tacked an additional reminiscence: 'Who afterwards, being in Germany – I believe at Innsbruck – and learning that the French were marching to attack the Low Countries, old and sick as he was, having dyed his beard and otherwise disguised himself, set off with only two or three attendants in order to reach the Provinces with the greater secrecy, which he would not have done, for he had already made two or three days' journey, had he not been seized with so violent a fit of gout that he could go no further, and was forced to turn back to the bed in which he had left Adrian, in whose presence Mass had been said and to whom meals had been brought, in order that the world might think the Emperor still there until his journey was nearly accomplished.'

Was this merely an example of the King's love of irrelevant detail and gossipy anecdotes or was it a concerted and subtle attempt to feed the flames of Don John's ambition of which Philip professed to be afraid? Don John needed no encouragement to imitate his father or to draw parallels between their actions. And why was Adrian Dubois, Charles V's chamberlain who, so the Emperor had once chosen to pretend, was Don John's father, unnecessarily mentioned? Even more importantly, who was the moving spirit in this curious four-handed diplomatic game? Was it Pérez, faithful to his old associate and fellow-pupil of Ruy Gómez, endeavouring to formulate a common foreign policy of which Ruy would have approved? Or was it the King, fearing his bastard brother's popularity and success, determined to place him in an impossible position where failure was almost inevitable and could always be ensured by the simple expedient of withholding sufficient money? Or was it in some way an attempt to involve Escovedo himself in responsibility for policy? The insistence that no one but Escovedo – not even the Pope – was to share with the King, Don John and Pérez the secret knowledge of the springs of European diplomacy was itself suspicious. Taken in conjunction with the arrangement that Don John should not under any circumstances be allowed to visit Madrid before he undertook the Governorship of the Netherlands, but could employ, if he wished, Escovedo as his Ambassador so that the two would soon necessarily be parted, the circumstance might have warned Escovedo of impending tragedy. But, unfortunately for himself, Escovedo was basically a simple man, who believed Antonio Pérez was still his friend and well-wisher and that King Philip could be trusted.

One thing at least Don John determined. He would treat Philip's appointment of him as Governor of the Netherlands as an order to be obeyed, but he would not take up the post until he had discussed the policy to be pursued privately and personally with Philip. He consulted the man who had the greatest knowledge and understanding of the situation in the Netherlands – Cardinal Granvelle, who had, on the Pope's behalf, delivered to him the banner of the Holy League and who became the chief adviser of Margaret, Duchess of Parma, the sister of King Philip and Don John, when for the eight stormy and disastrous years from 1559 to 1567 she had held the viceroyalty of the Netherlands. Granvelle, trained by the Emperor Charles V, was as able, versatile and indefatigable as he was selfish, crafty and unscrupulous. For the people of the Netherlands, he had an overwhelming contempt which caused him to refer to them as 'that animal'. His advice to Don John was that he should take care that he was given the fullest possible powers and that, without a plentiful supply of money, it was useless to go to the Low Countries at all. The real cause of the troubles was not religion but the weight of taxation.

Granvelle added that in society John should be gentle and in Council grave, as his father had been. His strength lay in the fact that he was the Emperor's son, but he must realise – as Philip seemed incapable of realising – that the Netherlanders of 1576, fierce and sore with the misgovernment and cruelties of twenty-one years, were not the same Netherlanders, prosperous and loyal, who had wept at the abdication of the Emperor in 1555.

Fortified by this advice, Don John wrote to his brother. On 27 May, Philip received, by the hand of Escovedo, a letter in which he professed his readiness to obey the royal orders in all things, but at the same time made it quite clear that he considered that in consenting to govern the Netherlands he was conferring, not receiving, a favour. The state of the Low Countries was nothing less than alarming. The King's enemies had consistently grown in strength; disaffection and heresy had made great progress and many of the King's ministers were implicated in the rebellious policy of the Estates. There was good reason to expect invasions from both England and France; the Provinces were wasted by the royal troops, whom the bankruptcy of the Exchequer forbade either payment or dismissal; the Spanish name was abhorred by the people and before he undertook to attempt to bring some order into this confusion, he was naturally most anxious to see the King in person so that he might receive from His Majesty's own lips instructions which neither letters nor ministers could convey. Since this had been denied him, he had sent Escovedo to Madrid in his stead. Meanwhile he entreated His Majesty that he might not be bound down by too rigid orders, but that he might be allowed a certain latitude of judgment, to act according to the shifting exigencies of the time and situation rather than to the strict letter of directions drawn up at a distance.

'One of the things which will most contribute to my mission,' he wrote, hoping ingenuously to allay his brother's neurotic jealousy, 'is that I should be held in esteem at home and that everyone should know and believe that as Your Majesty is unable to go to the Netherlands you have invested me with all the powers I could desire. Your Majesty knows that I shall use them for the re-establishment of your authority, now so fallen, to its proper place. And if Your Majesty is dissatisfied with the way in which I use my authority you can always resume the powers without fear of murmurs on my part or of opposition founded on my private interests.'

Philip replied by return that Don John must immediately abandon any idea of a personal meeting with him because of the great inconvenience it would cause him to have any change in the plans he had already formulated. 'Although I am well aware that as to this, and everything else, it is enough for you to be informed of my wishes only once, I think it proper to charge you a second time in no wise and for no reason whatsoever to think of visiting me.'

Clearly, Don John decided, he must visit him. He sailed to Spain with a fleet of three vessels and, on 22 August, from his barge in the roads of Barcelona, he sent Escovedo ashore to the Escorial, where the Court was, with a short letter to the King. He entreated Philip not to take amiss his coming to Spain, a step to which he had been impelled, so he said, 'not only by this desire to kiss His Majesty's hands, but by the interests of His Majesty's service, which were the guide of his conduct at all times, as Escovedo would more fully explain until he himself could reach Court'.

Don John arrived at the Escorial early in September 1576 and, despite his disobedience, was greeted affectionately by the King. But at the first audience an incident occurred which was indicative of the prevailing tension. After the brothers had embraced, John made a deep obeisance to the Queen, Philip's fourth wife, Anne of Austria, but it was his behaviour towards the six-year-old Infante, Don Fernando, that the Court was most keenly observing, for Escovedo had seen to it that one of Don John's requests was to be legitimated and raised to a rank on a par with that of the young prince. Before Don John turned to him, while he was still bowing to the Queen, the projecting metal tip, the chade, of his scabbard struck the small boy between the eyebrows bruising him and knocking him to the floor where his head struck with an impact which awakened memories of the fatal fall of Don Carlos, fifteen years before on the staircase at Alcalá.

The Infante was not seriously hurt, though this did not serve to cut short Don John's almost hysterical lamentations and apologies.

The King stopped him with: 'Enough! Give thanks to God it was no worse.'

'Worse, do you say?' replied his brother. 'There are windows here I can throw myself down from.'

'How can you speak like that?' said Philip, now gravely angry. 'Why should we have more than one misfortune?'

For the next fortnight meetings of the Council of State were held as well as private conversations between the brothers.

Into that part of the grand strategy which included the invasion of England from the Netherlands, the freeing of Mary Queen of Scots and her marriage to Don John and their installation as Queen Regnant and King Consort of England and Scotland, Philip now entered with enormous enthusiasm. It was a project which would turn all Don John's energies away from the Mediterranean, and so dispose of any possible rivalry. Philip even contemplated an alternative scheme that his brother might marry Elizabeth instead of Mary Queen of Scots. In any case, until it was time for the coup, Don John was to enter into the most amicable relations possible with the English Queen, to ascertain the exact amount and state of her naval and military resources and to take every means of corrupting her favourites and ministers.

Philip had much to say from his personal knowledge of his one-time sister-in-law, whose life he claimed to have saved during his reign as Mary Tudor's consort in England and whom, on Mary's death, he had thought of marrying himself. That was nearly twenty years ago, but, from ambassadorial reports, he was sure that certain characteristics had not changed. 'And as we quite well know,' he said familiarly to his brother, 'Elizabeth usually gets into correspondence and tries to establish relations with anyone she thinks she might perhaps marry. If this should happen to you, you must not appear backward, but let her run on as she pleases.'

Another family matter to be discussed concerned the attitude to be taken to Don John's mother, Barbara Blomberg. The Emperor, on his deathbed, had bestowed on her an annuity of two hundred florins. She had married a gentleman of the Court named Pyramus Kegel by whom she had two sons, but by now both Pyramus and the elder boy were dead and Barbara had been persuaded to leave Brussels and retire to Ghent, where she was provided with a house and an establishment consisting of a housekeeper and six women, a steward, a chaplain, four men-servants, two pages and an almoner. Here, surrounded by many suitors, she wasted her substance in riotous living.

Unavailing efforts had been made by Philip to induce her to retire to a convent in Spain. She said she quite understood how nuns were immured in such circumstances and that she would be cut to pieces rather than go there. Alba and Requesens, who had to deal with her as one of the minor but tiresome problems of their Governorship of the Netherlands had, in exasperation, planned to inveigle her into a vessel on pretence of going to Antwerp and then to take her by force across the Bay of Biscay.

Now, in this autumn of 1576, she was still living at Ghent, an unremoved thorn in Philip's side, awaiting the arrival of her famous son as Governor. Whatever she may have hoped, however, Don John, who disapproved of his mother's somewhat scandalous widowhood, had no intention of allowing her to remain in his dominions and Philip was satisfied before he and Don John left the Escorial for Madrid on 22 September that Barbara Blomberg would, by force if necessary, be sent to Spain for safe-keeping.

When the brothers returned to the capital, prayers were

ordered in all the churches for the safe journey of the new Governor to his seat of government. It was announced that he would travel by way of Barcelona and northern Italy, but because time was precious, it was secretly decided that he should take a more direct route. But first he went to Abrojo to take farewell of his beloved foster-mother who had a premonition that it was the last time she would see him. He was, according to the official time-table, to return to Madrid to take an official farewell of the royal family and be sped magnificently on his way to the Netherlands. But at Abrojo, according to secret instructions, he darkened his face and hands and blackened his fair beard and hair to disguise himself as a Moorish slave in the service of Ottavio Gonzaga. With them were two or three servants, including a French postillion whose knowledge of travel in France was said to be unique.

Don John wrote to the King on 14 October, when he arrived at the border, 'I have just arrived at Irun, never in my life having experienced such fatigue on a single journey for, horses being few, we have had to ride the same mount often for twelve leagues and sometimes for fifteen. I am only waiting for Ottavio who, to save time, went to Fuenterrabia while I came on here to have all things ready to proceed. A French merchant has just arrived who does not speak favourably of the safety of the roads; but I am neither doubtful nor apprehensive of pressing on, since there are so many reasons and obligations to do so.

'Now, Sir, the pressing matter is that you should conclude the arrangements for money and, along with that, send me Escovedo; for without those two things I do not know how to make a beginning. And as cases may arise in which you have said to aid me with your own blood if it would avail anything, I once more entreat Your Majesty to assist me with what I require *now* – which is money, money and more money, for without this it would have been better not to have hazarded so great a stake.

'Ottavio has just arrived and I therefore end my letter in order to proceed on our journey, praying Our Lord to keep Your Majesty in health and happiness.'

Escovedo, however, remained in Madrid, discussing with Antonio Pérez and the King the shambling, impractical plan of conquest, remote from all realities, which was to be imposed on Don John. Of the seventeen provinces of the Netherlands, fifteen were in open revolt; the royal army was in a state of mutiny; the rebel Hollanders commanded the estuaries and the sea; money, according to the King's own confession, 'was wanting here and everywhere' and the King's representative was stealing like a thief in the night into the country, which was governed, as far as it was governed at all, by the Prince of Orange and a National Committee.

Escovedo made no bones of his opinion. He called it *descosido* – 'unstitched'.

It was unfortunate that, at the same time, he discovered that Ana, Princess of Eboli, had decided to become Antonio Pérez's mistress.

X
Scandal in Madrid

The Princess of Eboli's vendetta against Teresa of Avila had soon come to nothing for lack of material. The only result of Ana's delation of the nun's autobiography to the Inquisition was that Teresa (who offered to burn the work) was ordered to make more copies of it for the edification of the pious. The foundation of her 'discalced' convents proceeded rapidly and, with the cooperation of King Philip, the Mother Foundress crossed from her native Castile into Andalusia and established a house in Seville itself.

At the time when Don John was preparing to leave Madrid, Fray Mariano was negotiating, on Mother Teresa's behalf, for the purchase of a 'little house' where members of her Order might stay when they had to visit the capital or the Court. The house was at some distance from the Eboli mansion nor, on other than geographical grounds, was there any likelihood that Ana and Teresa would meet. The Princess affected to be unaware of Teresa's existence. It was the best way to cover her defeat.

Madrid was still in the throes of building to give itself the appearance of a capital city, but the royal taxation, which was levied on all storeys of a house but the first, had had the effect of creating a multitude of meanness interrupted by disproportionate palaces advertising their owners' wealth. The courtiers referred to the one-storey houses as *construidas de malicia* – built with malice. A cynical French traveller remarked: 'The Spanish have taken their style of architecture from the moles; their houses are merely built of earth and, like molehills, only one storey high.'

Ana's palace, facing Great St. Mary's, was two storeys high, with a third storey over the gate-house facing the portico of the church. It contained over thirty rooms, most of them sumptuously furnished. In the Princess's bedroom, hung with tapestries, sparkling with gold, the bed was draped with green and gold damask, lined with silver brocade and trimmed with Spanish point-lace. The sheets were edged with lace fully half a yard wide. The other apartments, tapestried with crimson velvet and gold and the lesser rooms upholstered in white damask, were divided from each other by partitions of perfumed wood. The Princess entertained in a large gallery, richly carpeted and provided with cushions of crimson embroidered with gold and with cabinets of rare wood set with rows of precious stones. There were small silver tables and glass cabinets containing articles of extreme rarity and great intrinsic value, grey amber, porcelains, branches of coral, gold filigree and a thousand costly gems. In this Great Gallery there were sometimes as many as forty ladies, seated cross-legged on the ground, in imitation of the Moorish fashion, exchanging news and gossip. They sat in little groups of four or five together, round a little silver furnace full of olive-nuts, to prevent them getting headaches.

Not far from the Eboli palace was the mansion which Antonio Pérez had built for himself. 'La Casilla', which stood on the site at present occupied by the Convent of St. Elizabeth, in the street of the same name, was the wonder of the Madrid of that day. It is now hardly possible to imagine that it was then surrounded by shady gardens, big orchards, and by a green, dark wood more than a league in circumference. The house was large and square, with four towers at the corners, and its big windows with their beautifully wrought gratings opened in two symmetrical rows; the entrance was by a great paved courtyard, in which were rough-stone seats and two cisterns of granite and many iron rings, in the form of heads of wild beasts, horses and dogs, fixed in the wall for tying up animals. The dining-room and rooms for gaming and diversion were on the right hand; on the left were the guest chambers, and the front of the house was taken up by a suite of salons, furnished as no house belonging to a Grandee in Madrid was, with pictures, tapestries, Venetian glass, furniture of precious woods and massive silver and thousands of other valuable things, which made the house an object of wonder and gossip for the whole Court. This house, in which his own chamber was furnished exactly like the King's, was the scene of his great gambling parties with the High-Admiral of Castile and other Grandees, in which the play was so high that the first hand was four doubloons the stake and twenty doubloons the game. The Count of Fuensalida wrote of him as displaying more pomp than any Grandee. 'He has so many valets in his service that, on the days on which he does not dine at Court, they serve him with so much ostentation of lacquer, ivory and gold and silver plate as if he enjoyed an income of a thousand millions.' On the slightest journeys, Pérez travelled *en prince*. 'One day, going to Toledo, I met him at Torrejón, with coaches, carriages and litters, and accompanied by numerous followers on foot and horseback. His household furniture is estimated at 140,000 ducats.' So reported the captain of the King's Spanish Guard.

To amass this fortune and support this establishment, Pérez had not even to solicit bribes, but merely to take what was overwhelmingly offered by intelligent careerists at Court like the Italians who announced that they would rather give to Pérez all that they had been allotted to spend and considered themselves very lucky in knowing the means to succeed without having to wait about at Court.

Occasionally, of course, mistakes were made and Pérez assumed what was only a friendly loan was a given bribe – as in the case of the magnificent silver brazier Don John had lent him for a special occasion and for the return of which he was eventually sued for the 'sum of 700 ducats in exchange or the brazier in as good condition as when he had it'.

The gifts Pérez received from the Princess of Eboli (which included eight new counterpanes, embroidered in gold and silver on crimson velvet, two very valuable diamonds and a ring set with garnet worth several thousand crowns) were, of course, another matter altogether. It was quite understood, though not, of course, even faintly admitted, that these were lover's gifts – and the time was to come when he was ordered to return them.

The *affaire* between the two was not at first suspected. It was, after all, the most natural thing in the world for Pérez, who had all his life been brought up in the Gómez household, to continue to help and advise in any way he could, the widow and children of his dead master. Ana, to put the inquisitive off the scent, began to hint that Antonio was in fact Ruy's son; though this piece of scandal only prompted the malicious to observe that a touch of incest would not be likely to deter such a woman as La Tuerta.*

A likely obstacle, the courtiers said, was the possibility that the King was the father of Ana's eldest son, the Duke of Pastrana, and, though the boy was now eighteen and Philip's relations with Ana were anything but amorous, the overwhelmingly ambitious Pérez was unlikely to risk challenging, even retrospectively, the Royal jealousy.

Still another reason, was Pérez's preference for young men, which made the scandalous gossip about his household centre on the subject of his pages and which eventually resulted in his appearance before the Inquisition accused of sodomy.†

* La Tuerta: The One-Eyed Lady. In Spanish this may be taken in a moral as well as physical sense.

† At that period, the indulgence in sodomy might betoken belief in the Cathar heresy which held the only sexual sin to be reproduction. In the form of Priscillianism, it had been rife in Spain. The examination of the charge was thus a proper matter for the Inquisition to judge.

Ana herself was, by this time, almost impervious to gossip. Since Ruy's death, her life had taken a pattern which, in her occasional moments of self-searching, she could hardly recognise. She had done her best to cushion herself against the assaults of death when she had seen what ravages widowhood had inflicted on her aunt. She had made for herself, as she had thought, a retreat to holiness in 'her' Carmelite foundation at Pastrana. But when the testing time came, everything had collapsed. The intended good had turned to evil. And the Church, by its attitude to Mother Teresa and her writings, had implicitly condemned her, the 'saint of Avila's' accuser.

In returning to her ordinary life of gaiety in Madrid, Ana was prompted by something like desperation to try to find some means of coming to terms with existence. In taking for a lover the man who modelled himself on Ruy and whom she had known, as she had known Ruy, from her childhood, there was no insult to the memory of her beloved husband. Rather, if anything, the reverse. In the curious logic in which she lived, Antonio was a kind of extension of Ruy and the one criticism she passionately resented was Escovedo's reported outburst that she was showing, by her present conduct, how little she had cared for her husband when he had been alive.

This, however, was a mere beginning of his insults to her and as his anger and contempt increased, slight enough. He had never liked her even when, living for long periods in the house as Ruy's secretary, he had behaved with the scrupulous politeness due to his master's wife. It was possible that a kind of jealousy of Pérez, as the secretary more favoured by Ruy, played some part in his protests – so, at least, the gossips opined – but, to do him justice, it was genuine concern for Ruy's memory that motivated his actions. His indignation was kept at fever-heat by the reports with which he was regularly furnished by Rodrigo de Morgado, Pérez's intimate, who lived as a squire in his household and often acted as emissary between him and Ana.

One day, when Morgado had informed Escovedo that the lovers were together, he burst in and found them in bed. Beside himself with fury, he indulged in an uninhibited tirade the burden of which was how Ana had demeaned herself by allowing herself to be touched by so low a creature as Antonio Pérez, concluding with a threat that he would report the affair to the King.

This Ana cut brutally short with her often-quoted, and variously interpreted: 'Escovedo, do so if you like – I love Pérez's arse more than that of the King.' (*Que más quiero al trasero de Antonio Pérez que al Rey*.)

Next day the Princess and her lover determined that Escovedo should die.

XI
The Frustrations of Don John

Ana's cousin, Don Rodrigo de Mendoza, a Gentleman of the Chamber to King Philip, was Don John's most intimate friend and had been the only person for whom Don Carlos had had any genuine affection. Although Rodrigo had been in the dead Infante's service for only four months when the Prince was arrested by his father and committed to the custody of Ruy Gómez, one of Carlos's first questions had been whether 'his friend, Rodrigo' would be allowed to remain with him. Philip had replied that he could not spare Rodrigo from his own service and had insisted on parting the two, unmoved (if not, indeed, actually gratified) by his son's tears.

The affection which Rodrigo had inspired in Carlos, he also gave to and received from Don John who described him as 'his greatest friend'. For him he had 'a passionate affection' and he wrote to him continually and at some length during his enforced exile in the Netherlands.

When Don John first arrived in Luxembourg, he was sufficiently homesick for his letters to be mainly occupied with messages to his friends in Madrid urging them to keep him in mind. Even Ana was not overlooked. 'Kiss the hands of my one-eyed one for me (I do not say the eyes!) and until I can write to her myself, bid her not to forget this friend of hers who cannot in these parts offer, nor has means to offer, all he owes her.' But gradually, as Don John's frustration increased, his letters to Rodrigo became largely an easing of his own mind.

'The Spaniards are going away,' he wrote in the February of 1577, 'and they carry my soul with them for I had rather be bewitched than see this happen. It is for God to forgive the sorcery that goes on there and from which springs so much evil. In the meetings which have been held between the Netherlands States-General and me they have driven me so many times to lose my temper that, although I have kept it in countless cases, yet there have been others when I have lost it, and I have rated them roundly, telling them what they are and what they deserve, so that on every point we made ourselves useless to one another. They fear me and consider me a choleric person; and I abhor them and consider them very great scoundrels; and so it is needful now that I should go and another come in my place, for so sure as we meet, it is certain a new disagreement will arise and do mischief. I have therefore written home very urgently – let this be a secret between us – that I neither can nor will remain here any longer, since I have, by God's grace, accomplished that for which I came, which was to put an end to the war, according to the orders given me, when both parties were ready ranked one against the other.'

Negotiations became increasingly impossible but, what was worse, the rift between Don John and his brother, fomented by Pérez, grew wider. The essence of their differences lay in their disparate attitudes to religion. Don John was first and foremost a Catholic: Philip, however orthodox, however pious, was above all a King. It is hardly too much to say that whereas Don John was concerned to fight heresy, King Philip was intent on exerting his rule over heretics. Philip deliberately kept his brother short of men and money. 'I will not fail in the least of my duties,' John wrote to Don Rodrigo, 'but in the meantime I am angry that, turn where I may, only for me are wanting those great forces which abound here, in order, it would seem to drag me personally into the miserable plight in which they keep me. Yet I thank our Lord for giving me enough courage to endure this and to resolve not to be drowned in this deep water.'

Don John's letters to Philip asking for 'money, money, money – and Escovedo' were ignored. At the same time, his letters to Pérez (whom he imagined still to be his friend) were misrepresented to Philip by Antonio, who did all he could to poison the King's mind against his brother by stories which it is extraordinary that Philip could have believed. Don John, he said, was determined to make himself not only King of England but King of Spain. Once he had subdued the Netherlands, he would conquer England by means of Spanish troops and then turn the combined forces against Spain. His demand for 'money and Escovedo' was to be interpreted as money for the furthering of his traitorous plans in which his secretary was pledged to aid him.

Meanwhile, on 31 January 1578, Don John, unaware of the extent of the machinations at Madrid, had won a victory against the Dutch rebels at Gemblours. The standard which he had used at Lepanto he embellished with a cross and the legend, 'In this sign I defeated the Turks: in this sign I shall defeat the heretics' (*'In hoc signo vici Turcos: in hoc signo vincam haereticos'*) and, with inferior forces, gained an overwhelming victory in which the Spaniards lost not more than a dozen men and captured thirty-four standards, most of the artillery, vast quantities of baggage and inflicted thousands of casualties. In the letter reporting the victory to Rodrigo, John wrote: 'God himself knows how troubled I am to find myself so utterly unable to follow up the victory which He has given us as far as it might have been taken. I trusted the King to have provided me with what was needful; and, had he done so, Brussels would have been his as well as the greater part of these Provinces. But now the Provinces continue their rebellion and trifling little villages set themselves against us and cost us the blood of brave men. I am told that at Court there is no lack of people who say, if I am taken prisoner what would be lost or what would it matter? Let anyone who holds that opinion come here so that by what he avoids himself he may see what I have to do and how I shun no dangers except the contemptible ones nor can I ever withdraw from others!'

Don John's mental strain was added to by physical illness and when his nephew, Alexander Farnese, Duke of Parma, came to him in the Netherlands, he was shocked at his appearance. Parma, the son of Charles V's illegitimate daughter, Margaret, was three years older than his uncle. He had served under him at Lepanto and now took over from him the effective command of the army. A brilliant soldier, he reduced to obedience the whole province of Limburg within three weeks and with the loss of less than thirty of his men. But he loyally gave the credit to Don John, whom he loved and admired and with whom he shared the frustration caused by his other uncle, the King's, diplomatic delays.

'I desire more than life some decision on Your Majesty's part,' Don John wrote despairingly to Philip. 'Give me orders for the conduct of affairs. Our lives are at stake and all we ask is to lose them with honour.'

Philip scrawled in the margin of this letter: 'I will not answer.' Yet, after a fashion, he did answer. He consulted his confessor, Friar Diego de Chaves, as to whether it was permissible for him to order the death of a dangerous subject.

The friar told him: 'A prince who has power over the life of his subjects may, as he can deprive them of it for a just cause by formal judgment, also do it without due form, since judicial proceedings are no laws for him who may dispense with them.'

Fortified by this judgment, Philip ordered Pérez to kill Escovedo as soon as possible.

XII
Murder

One of Pérez's pages, Antonio Enríquez, recorded the killing: 'Being one day at leisure in the apartment of Diego Martínez, the major-domo of Antonio Pérez, Diego asked me whether I knew any of my countrymen who would be willing to stab a person with a knife. He added that it would be profitable and well paid, and that, even if death resulted from the blow, it was of no consequence. I answered that I would speak of it to a mule driver of my acquaintance, as in fact, I did; and the muleteer undertook the affair. Afterwards, Diego Martínez gave me to understand, with rather puzzling reasons, that it would be necessary to kill the individual, who was a person of importance, and that Antonio Pérez would approve of it; on this, I remarked that it was not an affair to be trusted to a muleteer, but to persons of a better stamp. Then Diego Martínez added that the person to be killed often came to the house, and that, if we could put anything in his food or drink, we must do so; because that was the best, surest, and most secret means. It was resolved to have recourse to this method, and with all dispatch.

'During these transactions, I had occasion to go to Murcia. Before my departure, I spoke of it to Martínez, who told me I should find, in Murcia, certain herbs well adapted to our purpose; and he gave me a list of those which I was to procure. In fact, I sought them out and sent them to Martínez, who had provided himself with an apothecary, whom he had sent for from Molina in Aragon. It was in my house that the apothecary, assisted by Martínez, distilled the juice of those herbs. In order to make an experiment of it afterwards, they made a cock swallow some, but no effect followed; and what they had thus prepared, was found to be good for nothing. The apothecary was then paid for his trouble, and sent away.

'A few days after, Martínez told me he had in his possession a certain liquid fit to be given to drink, adding that Antonio Pérez, the secretary, would trust nobody but me, and that, during the repast that our master was to give in the country, I should only have to pour out some of this water for Escovedo, who would be among the guests, and for whom the preceding experiments had already been tried. I answered that unless my master himself gave me the order, I would not have a hand in poisoning anybody. Then Secretary Antonio Pérez called me one evening in the country, and told me how important it was for him that Secretary Escovedo should die; that I must not fail to give him the beverage in question on the day of the dinner; and that I was to contrive the execution of it with Martínez; adding, moreover, good promises and offers of protection in whatever might concern me.

'I went away very contented, and consulted with Martínez as to the measures to be taken. The arrangement for the dinner was as follows: entering the house by the passage of the stables, which are in the middle, and advancing into the first room, we found two sideboards, one for the service of plates, and the other for that of the glasses, from which we were to supply the guests with drink. From the said room, on the left, we passed to that where the tables were laid, and the windows of which looked out on the country. Between the rooms where they were to dine, and that where the sideboards stood, was a square room, serving as antechamber and passage. Whilst they were eating, I was to take care that, every time Secretary Escovedo asked for drink, I should be the person to serve him. I had thus the opportunity of giving him some twice; pouring the poisoned water into his wine at the moment I passed through the antechamber, about a nutshellful, as I had been ordered. The dinner over, Secretary Escovedo went away, but the others remained to play, and, Antonio Pérez having gone out for a moment, rejoined his major-domo and me in one of the apartments over the courtyard, where we gave him an account of the quantity of water that had been poured into Secretary Escovedo's glass; after which he returned to play. We heard, afterwards, that the beverage had produced no effect.

'A few days subsequent to this ill success, Secretary Antonio Pérez gave another dinner in what is called Cordon House, which belonged to the Count of Puñon Rostro, where Secretary Escovedo, Doña Juana Coëllo, the wife of Pérez, and other guests were present. Each of them was served with a dish of milk or cream, and in Escovedo's was mixed a powder like flour. I gave him, moreover, some wine mixed with the water of the preceding dinner. This time it operated better, for Secretary Escovedo was very ill, without guessing the reason. During his illness, I found means for one of my friends, the son of Captain Juan Rubio, governor of the principality of Melfi, and formerly Pérez's major-domo (which son, after having been page to Doña Juana Coëllo, was a scullion in the king's kitchens), to form an acquaintance with Secretary Escovedo's cook, whom he saw every morning. Now, as they prepared for the sick man a separate broth, this scullion, taking advantage of a moment when nobody saw him, cast into it a thimbleful of a powder that Diego Martínez had given him. When Secretary Escovedo had taken some of this food, they found that it contained poison. They subsequently arrested one of Escovedo's female slaves who must have been employed to prepare the pottage; and, upon this proof, they hanged her in the public square at Madrid, though she was innocent.

'Secretary Escovedo having escaped all these plottings, Antonio Pérez adopted another plan; namely, that we should kill him some evening with pistols, stilettoes, or rapiers, and that without delay. I started, therefore, for my country, to find one of my intimate friends, and a stiletto with a very thin blade, a much better weapon than a pistol for murdering a man. I travelled post, and they gave me some bills of exchange of Lorenzo Spinola at Genoa, to get money at Barcelona, and which, in fact, I received on arriving there.'

Here Enríquez relates that he enticed into the plot one of his brothers, named Miguel Bosque, to whom he promised a sum of gold and the protection of Pérez; that they arrived at Madrid the very day Escovedo's slave was hanged; that, during his absence, Diego Martínez had fetched from Aragon, for the same object, two resolute men, named Juan de Mesa and Insausti; that the very day after his arrival, Diego Martínez had assembled all four, as well as the scullion Juan Rubio, outside Madrid, to decide as to the means and moment of the murder; that they had agreed upon this; that Diego Martínez had procured them a sword, broad and fluted up to the point, to kill Escovedo with, and had armed them all with daggers; and that Antonio Pérez had gone, during that time, to pass Holy Week at Alcalá, doubtless with the intention of turning suspicion from him when the death of Escovedo was ascertained.

Enríquez continues: 'It was agreed, that we should all meet every evening upon the little square of Saint James, whence we should go and watch on the side by which Secretary Escovedo was to pass; which was done. Insausti, Juan Rubio, and Miguel Bosque, were to waylay him; while Diego Martínez, Juan de Mesa, and I, were to walk about in the neighbourhood, in case our services should be required in the murder.

'On Easter Monday, 31 March, the day the murder was committed, Juan de Mesa and I were later than usual in repairing to the appointed spot, so that, when we arrived at St. James's Square, the four others had already started to lie in ambush for the passing of Secretary Escovedo. Whilst we were loitering about, Juan de Mesa and I heard the report that Escovedo had been assassinated. We then retired to our lodgings. Entering my room, I found Miguel Bosque there, in his doublet, having lost his cloak and pistol; and Juan de Mesa found, likewise, Insausti at his door, who had also lost his cloak, and whom he let secretly into his house.

'It was Insausti who had struck Escovedo. He had despatched him at one blow with the sword which Diego Martínez had given him, and which Juan de Mesa and he then flung into the well of the house they inhabited. The same night Juan Rubio went over to Alcalá, to inform Pérez of what had passed; who hearing that nobody had been arrested, rejoiced greatly.'

The murderers were, naturally, protected from prosecution and duly rewarded. The country boy, Miguel Bosque, received a hundred crowns in gold from the hands of one of Pérez's clerks. Mesa, the oldest, an Aragonese landholder and from a long time in the past a friend of the Pérez family, was given a gold chain, fifty pieces of eight and a silver cup. To facilitate his escape back to his estate in Aragon (where he came under the protection of the jealously guarded *fueros* – as Pérez himself was ultimately to do) Ana gave him a certificate designating him her under-steward at Pastrana. This acted as a passport for the first stage of his flight, for Pastrana lay on the way to safety. The *bravo*, Insausti, the actual murderer, the page Enríquez and Juan Rubio, the scullion, were all appointed ensigns in His Majesty's army with additional annual pensions of twenty gold crowns; and Philip signed their commissions as a matter of course. However, gossip was swift in reaching the true mark and it was not long before Ana was writing to the King; 'Some slanderers are going so far as to say that Pérez procured the death of Escovedo on my account! Since these people are daring enough to have gone to such lengths, Your Majesty is, as a King and a gentleman, obliged to make such an example of them that the report of it may spread wherever the slander is known. If Your Majesty should not be thus minded, but would like my house to be lost, together with the fortune of my ancestors and the well-deserved favour of the prince my late husband, if their services are to be repaid with such a return and such a reward, I shall at least, by speaking to you as I do, have fulfilled my duty to myself. I entreat Your Majesty to return this letter to me, as what I say is only for a gentleman whose discretion I trust – with all the resentment that such indignity deserves.'

Philip neither returned nor answered the letter and Ana was forced to rely on Pérez to plead for the King's continued support.

'He has given me his word of honour as a king and a gentleman that he will never betray me,' he told Ana.

'His casuistry will extricate him from that,' she answered. 'If I know Philip, he will let you wear the criminal's cap alone if there is any chance of it being fitted on his head.'

When Pérez repeated this to Philip, the King replied: 'You must be out of your mind to imagine such a thing.'

But Ana was not convinced and when she heard that Mateo Vázquez, another of the King's secretaries, had written to Philip: 'Sire, people suspect your Secretary Pérez of being the author of Secretary Escovedo's death on account of a woman', she knew panic and pleaded with her lover to bring things to a head.

'Are all our friends safely abroad?' she asked him.

'Yes, indeed,' he replied. 'Rubio is in Milan, Enríquez in Naples, Insausti himself is in Sicily, Bosque, as you know, is in Saragossa and –'

'In other words, no one can call them as witnesses?'

'No, not even that envious, interfering fool, Vázquez.'

'Then, Antonio, why not force the issue?'

'How?'

'Resign your Secretaryship and insist on a process to put an end to these slanders.'

Pérez, one of whose maxims was that attack was always the best form of defence, agreed at once and proposed the plan to Philip.

The King was alarmed at so dangerous a course and refused absolutely to adopt it. As a concession to Pérez's importunity, however, he suggested that the Bishop of Córdova, President of the Council of Castile, should be told the circumstances of the murder under the seal of confession and be asked to set at rest the suspicions of Vázquez and of Escovedo's son, Pedro.

Accordingly the Bishop sent for Pedro and said to him: 'Señor Don Pedro Escovedo, the King has handed over to me the memorial of yourself and your mother, in which you demanded justice for the death of your father, against Antonio Pérez and the Princess of Eboli. His Majesty commands me to tell you that you shall have full justice, without any respect of persons, rank, sex, or condition. But I ought first to engage you to examine well what grounds or convincing testimony you have to establish your proofs, and whether they be of a nature to exculpate you from the offence you would give to persons of such consideration. For, if these proofs are not very sufficient and do not justify your complaint, the demonstration will turn against yourself; the Princess, being the person she is, and her condition and very high quality being worthy of so much respect, and Antonio Pérez being also what he is, the descendant of fathers and ancestors for ages servants of the Crown and occupying the high office with which he is now invested. Lastly, and before you answer me, I will also tell you confidentially, and I affirm upon my word as a priest, that the Princess and Antonio Pérez are as innocent as I am.'

Suitably impressed, Pedro promised to pursue the matter no further.

But Mateo Vázquez continued in his suspicions.

XIII
The End of Don John

Don John on hearing of Escovedo's death wrote immediately to his brother: 'Sir, With greater grief than I can describe, I have heard of the unhappy death of Secretary Escovedo, for which I cannot find, nor shall I ever find, any consolation because your Majesty has lost such a servant as I know him to have been, and I such a one as your Majesty also knows that he was. And although there is in this sufficient cause for the sorrow which I feel, above all else I lament that at the end of so many years and services he should meet with a death so unworthy of him, and caused by his having served his King with so much truth and love, and without any of those other aims and without the craft which is now in fashion. Even at its worst, it is my opinion that nothing should be rashly judged; but yet I do not think that in this case I incur blame when I say that I point at no one in particular, but believe that there is no doubt the affair is, as I have said. As one to whom so many opportunities of knowing were given, and who did know the independent manner in which Escovedo bore himself in the service of your Majesty, I am much afraid of the quarter whence the blow came. After all, I do not certainly know it, nor, knowing it, would I say more than this, that for the love of Our Lord I entreat your Majesty as lovingly as I can that you will not permit such an outrage to happen in your Court, or so great an affront to be done to me as that which has been done, without using every possible diligence to know whence the blow came and to punish it with the rigour which it deserves. And although I believe your Majesty has already done this very completely, being so Christian and justice-loving a Prince, yet I nevertheless beg it of you, feeling that I ought as a gentleman to take care of the honour of one who so truly deserved it of me, as did Escovedo, and to whom I am under obligations so great that I may with just reason consider myself to have been the cause of his death, as your Majesty knows better than any other person.

'May your Majesty therefore be pleased, I pray, to approve of my not only reminding you of the affairs of the deceased, but soliciting you, as I will do by every post, with regard to them until entire justice shall have been done, and remuneration for his services made, and of my even letting other things stand still, as I ought, as a gentleman, to do.

'All this I once more entreat your Majesty as humbly and earnestly as I can, and that your Majesty will be pleased to order answers to be sent to me on these various points; for I confess to your Majesty that nothing can now happen to trouble my spirit like this death, until everything which concerns the deceased has been arranged. As to his worldly affairs I do not yet know how he has left them, so of none of them can I speak in particular; but I pray your Majesty will remember the desire of Escovedo, which was ever to serve your Majesty honourably and with clean hands, and the poor house which he leaves behind him, and that you will show the kindness which they deserve to those who remain in it; and especially that you will confer upon his eldest son the places and emoluments possessed by his father. That these will be well bestowed upon Pedro de Escovedo, and that he is a man whose merits will every day grow with the employment and favour which he may receive, no one knows better than your Majesty.

'Considering the position Escovedo was obliged to maintain, and his small income, I think it likely that he may have left some debt, which may trouble the repose of his soul, and also weigh upon his children and his wife. I therefore ask your Majesty to make them a grant by which these debts may be paid off. But my chief request is, that as I find myself in the place of father, as it were, to the eldest son, you will do me the signal favour of giving him all those emoluments which his father enjoyed. As to the debts, I can easily arrange to defray the most of those which are for food and clothing, and to provide for the payment of those which are most pressing, which is the least that I can do for the case of one who laboured until his death, and died, to afford me repose and that good assurances as to the service of your Majesty, in all matters that passed through his hands, which I have ever desired and shall desire all my life.

'It is for your Majesty to see whether these obligations deserve that these offices should be given in requital of them, and whether I have a right to be confident that the favour which I beg will be granted to me, in regard to all that I have sued for and shall continue to sue for, until that justice and grace are obtained for which the blood and services of the dead are always pleading. May Our Lord keep your Majesty in the welfare and ease which I desire and need. From Beaumont, on the 20th of April 1578.'

Don John was not mistaken in imagining that the murder of Escovedo was a warning to him and, if he was forced to doubt whether Philip could actually contemplate fratricide, the fate of Don Carlos was a reminder that the King had not shrunk from killing his son from the highest political motives. To Rodrigo, Don John wrote on 28 July 1578: 'His Majesty keeps me much closer than any Christian deserves to be kept, even were he one of those bad ones now in fashion and I deserve it less than any other, since he never had a will so near his own or a man so willing to be sacrificed at his good pleasure.'

It was another two months before Don John was sacrificed. For a short time it seemed, paradoxically, that Elizabeth of England would do Philip's work for him. It had been suggested that instead of marrying Mary Queen of Scots, Don John should marry Elizabeth and thus as a missionary-husband lead England back to the Faith. The idea of marriage had originated with the Queen in one of her political and personal coquetries, and Don John had never given any sanction to the preposterous scheme but had received her advances with a cold and distant courtesy which she did not approve and to which she was certainly not accustomed. She openly expressed considerable disapproval of what she termed the slight put upon her by a Spanish bastard and, sending to the Tower for a condemned murderer named Ratcliffe, she offered him freedom and a reward if he assassinated Don John. The Spanish Ambassador in London, however, got wind of the plot and sent Don John a portrait of the murderer, who when he arrived at Namur was duly arrested and imprisoned.

Towards the end of September Don John became increasingly ill and, foreseeing his end, appointed Parma to succeed him as Governor-General and Commander-in-Chief of the Low Countries until Philip's pleasure was known. He had himself carried from Namur to the battle lines of the regiment at Figueroa. With characteristic self-sacrifice he refused to have any of the officers turned out of their quarters to make room for him and he was housed in an old pigeon house which was cleaned and made as habitable as possible. Here he directed his confessor, Fr. Francisco Orantes, to make public what he had already told him privately: that he left no will because he possessed nothing which was not his Lord and Master, the King's; that he commended his body and soul to the King – 'his soul in order that the King should order suffrages (intercessory prayers) to be made for the great need there was for them, his body that it might be buried near that of his Lord and Father the Emperor by which he would consider his services were repaid . . . as to my personal debts and bills,' he said at the end, 'they are very few and very clear.'

He showed his friend Fr. Fernández a little manuscript book which he kept under his pillow, saying these were the prayers he had recited every day of his life without missing one, and as the dreadful pain in his head troubled his sight he begged the father for the love of God and for the love of him to recite them in his name. Much moved the father did so, and, according to his testimony, it took him a good hour to recite what the devout prince had said daily for himself 'in the midst of the fatigues of war, the occupations of Governor, and, most difficult, in the midst of the dissipations of worldly pleasure'.

The little book was in Don John's own hand and began with the prayers he had learnt in his childhood, then followed various pious exercises, and it ended with several prayers composed by Don John himself and inspired by his difficulties, hopes, sorrows, joys and by his warm desire to give thanks. In short it was an index of his attitude towards God in all the events of his life.

In one of his earlier conversations with Fr. Fernández Don John had spoken of his firm determination, taken four months before, to retire for ever from the world to the hermitage of Montserrat – if God spared his life in Flanders – there to serve 'that Lord who could and would do much more for him than his brother Philip' thus revealing the profound disillusionment which had taken hold of the victor of Lepanto since the death of Escovedo.

His last conscious act was to hear Mass, and though his sight was gone and he had not the strength to move, he had himself raised from the bed and managed to turn his head to adore the elevated Host before he fell back in a coma from which he did not recover.

The post-mortem revealed that 'the side of his breast was yellow and black, as if burnt, and crumbled at a touch', but this evidence of poison was too dangerous to be generally admitted. Only Don John's confessor and Brantôme, who was protected by his French nationality, did not scruple to say openly that the prince had been poisoned by Philip's orders.

One of Don John's pleas to Philip had been that he might be buried near their father in the Escorial. Accordingly the following spring the King of Spain obtained leave from the King of France for a party of Don John's followers to return to Madrid by way of his country, though the actual reason was not disclosed. They were in fact the bearers of Don John's body which had been cut in pieces at the joints and put in three leather bags which were carried on the pack-saddle of a horse like any other baggage. On arrival in Spain the several portions were reassembled and the body stuffed and dressed as in life, erect and leaning on a general's staff. So, for the last time, Philip gazed at his brother while the few courtiers privileged to attend the bizarre ceremony watched hawkeyed the reaction of their sovereign. Pérez was satisfied that the King's passivity of countenance betrayed nothing though Ana, who knew nothing of the true circumstances, was intrigued to notice that the King's eyes were fixed not on but beyond the dead man's face.

Next day the body of the nonpareil Prince was buried with due pomp and ceremony near the tombs of the Emperor Charles V and Don Carlos.

XIV
Lèse-Majesté

That Philip II countenanced, indeed ordered Escovedo's murder and promised to protect the perpetrators is indisputable. He did so because already Pérez had convinced him that Don John was a threat to his person and to the State, and that Escovedo was the Prince's evil genius. But Pérez's reasons for fearing Escovedo were more weighty than at first appeared. Certainly he and Ana had determined that Escovedo should die following the secretary's furious and uninhibited tirade against them when he had threatened to tell the King of what he had seen in the Princess's bedroom in Madrid, but the danger Escovedo represented went far beyond that.

Escovedo had come to Madrid from Flanders in the summer of 1577 to discover why the King had been so dilatory in answering Don John's demands for help in the war with Flanders. By the time Pérez and Ana decided to have him killed he was on the point of discovering that Pérez had been intriguing against him and Don John and that he had been doing this in part by abusing the permission Don John had given him to alter Don John's ciphered messages in whatever way Pérez judged would help the Prince. Moreover Escovedo knew that Pérez had been secretly in touch with Italians, Dutch, French, and Portuguese behind Philip's back, taking bribes and influencing his master in their interest rather than in that of the State. Escovedo knew of some of these intrigues – he had been party to some of them – and he knew enough to topple Pérez if he chose. Once certain that Pérez was plotting against Don John and himself he would certainly have revealed all he knew.

Turning Philip against Escovedo had not been difficult with all the opportunities Pérez had and his understanding of his master's naturally suspicious and devious mind. Escovedo too was proud, even arrogant in manner, and his indignant and desperate letters to the King asking for money and arms for Don John also helped Philip, thus prompted, to think of him as more than ambitious in his master's interest. What therefore remains to be explained is not why Philip acted against Escovedo and Don John, but why he later turned against Pérez and Ana.

During the spring of 1579, a year after the murder of Escovedo, Don John's papers arrived in Madrid. From these Philip began to understand the true nature of the relationship between Don John and Escovedo on one side and Pérez and Ana on the other. Here it must be admitted that speculation plays a part for having studied Don John's papers Philip destroyed them – an uncharacteristic action from a monarch who, whatever else he achieved, left a mountain of paper behind him – yet entirely explicable: if the papers showed beyond reasonable doubt Don John's innocence of any design against Philip and his legitimate possessions.

Philip had no scruples against murder where his conscience, in line with the direction of his confessor, indicated that the safety of the realm, of his person, or the inviolability of the Faith demanded such a measure. A long line of theologians and jurists supported this view. But what if the murder turned out not to have been justified at all? He must then have questioned his motives in allowing himself to be misled by the duplicity of his secretary. Might he not have decided that his own envy and unreasonable fear of his brother had inclined him wilfully to a too easy and fatal credulity? Such thoughts would have been enough to turn him irreconcilably against his secretary.

Don John's papers would have shown his innocence, or, where guilt there was, its exact and limited extent. They would have confirmed what Philip already suspected, that Don John had been negotiating for support from the Pope to free and marry Mary Queen of Scots – a plan Philip himself had canvassed in the past; that he was in touch with the Guises and the League, scarcely criminal in the Champion of Christendom. The most damaging would have been the truth concerning an idea the King already knew of through Pérez, who had no doubt presented it in a far worse light than it now appeared. A letter Escovedo wrote to Perez before he knew he had anything to fear from his old colleague gives the outline: 'You and Los Vélez (Philip's chief minister and now leader of the Eboli party) must sorrow over the tasks His Majesty is undertaking and how much need there is to look to his health for on it depends that of His Highness*. For this reason and because the Lord our Prince is a child, it would be fitting to have someone who could make the King's burdens easier. And having seen the sagacity, prudence and judiciousness with which His Excellency Don John directs these affairs in Flanders it seems he is a person worthy that trust. As Scripture says "God was pleased to give the King this staff in his old age . . ." '

Clearly a design of this sort can be presented in two very contrasting lights, and Pérez doubtless revealed it to the King as a plot to superannuate the monarch and make Don John Regent during the minority of the Prince with who knows what consequences if the Prince did not survive. However taken in the context of all Don John's papers, with his correspondence with Escovedo entire, it could have

* This was Philip (b. 1578), second son of Philip II by Ann of Austria and brother of Fernando who had been knocked to the ground by Don John's scabbard. Fernando had died the year before. Philip succeeded his father as Philip III in 1598.

seemed harmless, even well meaning. Beyond this – and considering Don John's lineage, position, and reputation, Philip can hardly have expected less – his brother was innocent.

The papers would have uncovered more, namely the facts suggested in the ninth charge eventually laid, many years later, against Pérez: 'That when the said Escovedo came to the capital, the accused, Antonio Pérez, feared that Escovedo would discover the aforesaid transgressions and falsehoods, and determined to have him killed . . .' that is that Pérez sold state secrets, had illicit correspondence with Escovedo, and had abused the licence Don John had given him to alter his ciphered messages.

There is no doubt that Ana was deeply involved too – she inspired many of Pérez's schemes and colluded with him in concocting them. Her relationship with Antonio was now revealed to be far more than amatory, and the lavish gifts she showered on him were rewards for services indeed performed behind closed doors – but not, or not only, in bed. This explains why Pérez was forced to return all, or nearly all, when he was eventually found guilty of corruption, that is of political corruption.

Ana once said to her companions: 'It is a wearisome thing for lords to be always lords.' 'Why?' she was asked. 'Because it angers me they should be always lords and never kings.' As the wife of Ruy Gómez she no doubt believed, when not occupied with her ten children, that she actually had some influence on the course of events, such was the splendid tact with which he had handled her. Her first resort at his death – to become a nun – had been foiled by her own wilfulness and the firmness of Teresa of Avila, and indeed with the wider publication of the Saint's autobiography the final outcome had been humiliating; her second resort was to return to Madrid, where Antonio Pérez was on the way to becoming as powerful as her husband had been, and whose vanity, extravagance and love of intrigue made him a far more vulnerable and ready accomplice than her husband in her ambition to figure as a power in the land. Of this time, when she and Pérez together seemed almost to rule in Madrid, when the ostentation of their lives and establishments surpassed the King's, she said: 'Though my husband is dead, I know and can perform more than ever – especially in the affairs of Flanders and Italy.'

In short, through the spring and early summer of 1579, Philip became more and more, but always privately, convinced that Ana and Pérez were together guilty of that most pernicious of crimes – pernicious that is to an absolute monarch – *lése-majesté*, by taking on themselves prerogatives that only a King should exercise. Just how far Ana and Pérez had gone we shall learn. The problem facing Philip was how to deal with them.

Doubtless a different monarch would have moved swiftly, lopped off their heads, and then weathered the ensuing storm – confident that in removing the leaders of a faction, the nucleus round which a party might form either out of self-interest or in sincere horror at tyranny, the shock and scandal of sudden retribution would be a nine days' wonder soon forgotten as the pattern of privilege and patronage in the Court and government adapted itself to new circumstances. But that was never Philip's way. He proceeded against Ana and Pérez slowly, deviously, with many apparent twists and changes of course, but finally as inexorably as the sudden quietus of an axe-blade – moreover, it may well be that in the long run the lingering wretchedness of both, and the sufferings of their families and connections in the coming two decades, exceeded what they would have borne if the King's vengeance had been swift.

Yet Philip had good reasons to proceed slowly, reasons that can be grouped under four headings. First, whatever Pérez's faults, he had become a necessary, an almost indispensable part of the machinery of government; moreover, his master had come to rely on him as a skilled, informed, often brilliant adviser on the affairs of the huge and complex web of states and principalities, each with its own constitution and interests, that made up Philip's domains – to call it an Empire is to imply a cohesion, a uniformity, that it never had. To remove at a stroke the man who sat at the very centre of this web, holding in his hands the destiny of projects, alliances, hostilities, and finances in Flanders, Italy, and Portugal was to invite chaos.

Secondly, the removal of Pérez would involve (finally did involve) the end of the Eboli party, the survivors and inheritors of Ruy Gómez's ministry. Allied by blood and marriage to Ana and to Pérez or out of habit, self-interest, or sincere support of his policies were such important figures in the government as the Marquis of Los Vélez (the leader of the party and virtually of the government), the Marquis of Mondéjar, the Duke of Medina Sidonia, the Archbishop of Toledo, and the powerful Aragonese nobility led by the Duke of Villahermosa and the Count of Aranda – such a party had to be destroyed piecemeal allowing the wasting process of age, failure, and natural death to reduce it until thirteen years later, in 1592, the rump was sufficiently powerless to be dealt with more ruthlessly.*

The third reason was Ana's lineage – her powerful connections spread far beyond merely party interests. Ana de Mendoza y la Cerda, Duchess of Pastrana, was related by blood and marriage to most of the grandees of Castile, whose pride in blood, in caste, has always been, and still remains today, the very type of aristocratic exclusiveness, and who had lost in the previous century the immense political power that went with feudal lordships and vassalage – and they still resented the loss: yet they held enormous wealth, enormous estates, and controlled the lives of countless retainers. While the principle and sanctity of Monarchy was

* Villahermosa and Aranda were poisoned in prison following the Aragon Revolt – see final chapters of the present volume. Philip preferred poison as it gave the victims time to make a full act of contrition.

the very base of this caste's beliefs, it remained a possibility that the peremptory execution, without formal arraignment and trial, of one of its most illustrious members (illustrious that is in blood and lineage) and she a woman, might at the least dangerously alienate this caste, and at the worst serve to provide a cause and focus for revolt.

The final reason for Philip's caution was simply that Pérez knew too much, and was in possession of documents that proved what he knew – the story of the next ten years is largely the story of Philip's attempts to extricate these documents from Pérez's possession – by threats, bribes, offers of reconciliation, and finally by torture; and of Pérez's desperate determination to cling on to them, as the last safeguard of his and his family's lives. On the face of it, following the evidence of the inquiries and trials of Pérez these documents were simply those that implicated Philip in the murder of Escovedo, and were the basis of Pérez's defence for that crime, but there must have been many more and of more note – some perhaps relating to the deaths of Baron Montigny in Simancas, of Queen Isabella, of the Marquis of Poza, of Don Carlos, and perhaps of Don John himself, and others too, relating to equally embarrassing, if not so immediately sensational matters. To some of all this Pérez made reference later in his life when safe in exile in Béarn, England and France, but he never accused Philip in writing – and for a good reason: although he was safe (except from assassination), his wife and children remained, throughout Philip's life, imprisoned hostages for his good behaviour.

And so the ruin of Pérez and Ana had to be gradual – and for the first months after the arrival of Don John's papers, Philip was content to wait until he was sure of the outcome, certain of a Minister to take over the formation of a new, anti-Eboli government. Meanwhile he was content to allow others to proceed for him to whom he gave clandestine and unofficial encouragement. That Escovedo's family demanded justice and retribution caused Ana and Pérez no loss of sleep at all – but when Pedro Escovedo, the Secretary's son, found an ally in the ministry, almost as close to Philip as Pérez himself, their complacence turned first to unease and then to sharp concern.

XV
Arrest

The man who brought Philip the news of Escovedo's assassination on 31 March 1578 was Mateo Vázquez, another of the King's Principal Secretaries. Mateo was of humble origin and unknown parentage, having been brought up as a child by Diego Vázquez Alderete, then a canon of Seville Cathedral, whose name he took. Mateo claimed that his parents were Corsicans, that his pregnant mother had been kidnapped by Algerian pirates, that he had been born in Algiers. He and his mother, he said, were ransomed to Seville where they came under the protection of the canon. Through tireless application and a reputation for absolute loyalty he rose quickly and by the time he was twenty-two was a secretary of Espinosa, Cardinal Bishop of Sigüenza, President of the Council of Castile, who ordained him. Apparently Mateo was relatively incorruptible too – when the Cardinal died and he entered the King's service, he resigned the benefices the Cardinal had given him. In 1578 he had been a Principal Secretary for five years and was thirty-five years old.

Mateo Vázquez was as different from Pérez as a mule from a thoroughbred and doubtless this was one of the reasons for his advancement – as we have seen, the King made a point of choosing ministers, advisers, and secretaries who would at the best complement each other and in fact were so antipathetic to each other that alliances between them were out of the question. Mateo was plebeian in face, squat in stature, sober in dress and manners. He was persevering, studious, meticulous, orderly – few people understood so well the mechanics of Philip's bureaucracy – and dull. He was also a tale-bearer and a hypocrite, and no doubt justified himself as such since to his mind nothing could merit reproach if it was done, or could be shown to have been done, in the King's service.

It seems certain that in the first place he had no knowledge at all of either Philip's or Pérez's part in the murder – and though Mateo was a personal secretary this is quite in keeping with Philip's secretive habits for no one was ever completely in his confidence. Thus when rumour pointed its finger at Pérez and Ana as the assassins it was Mateo Vázquez who carried the tale to Philip, and when Pedro Escovedo came to Court demanding justice on his father's murderers it was Mateo Vázquez who encouraged and directed him – no doubt with the King's approval – to lay his charges before the President of the Council of Castile. By the end of the year (1578) Pérez and Ana were convinced that Vázquez was the leader and mastermind of a faction against them: and Vázquez – apparently bewildered by the hornets' nest he had stirred up – feared for his life: what had happened to Escovedo could well, he thought, happen to him. The animosity between the two secretaries increased steadily into the spring and early summer of 1579 and soon became a public disgrace – ambassadors reporting back to their capitals spoke of open factions, of fighting in the streets between retainers; the affair was the subject of gossip throughout the capital, and people began to talk openly of taking sides – and the general opinion was that the fault lay with Pérez and Ana.

In March, Mateo pleaded with the King: 'The business of government is threatened by this feud, which is not my making, for people say I have blocked appointments that should have been made simply because the people concerned were friends of Pérez. And truly, he shows great animosity towards me in public. The President of the Council says there is no remedy to be found unless Your Majesty intervenes with a powerful hand . . .' To which the King soothingly but vaguely replied: 'I shall attend to it and try to seek a remedy; I think I shall do what is befitting, so you attend to your business and what concerns you in it without bothering about these matters or the fortunes of other people.' Mateo was not so easily soothed – he was, by now, a truly frightened man and produced as evidence that his fears were justified the following statement made by a friendly cleric. It seems contrived, and clumsily so at that, but it is significant that Mateo felt driven to such contrivances.

'Declaration of Fr. Pedro de Royuela

'On the day of the Holy Sacrament, 18 June of the year '79, a man whom I have neither seen nor met before, confessed with me. Among other things he warned me that certain people were angry with Sr Mateo Vázquez, an ecclesiastic in the house of Your Majesty, and to such an extent that if they had been able to put him to death they would have done so. The penitent said that he was very friendly with these people and had been informed of it by them; they had induced him to help in the matter and he had promised to do so. He told me that I should warn the said Mateo Vázquez to be careful on the roads both day and night for they were to be looking out for him at inns and on the road.

'The said man told me that if the opportunity arose even on the very day of Corpus Christi they would carry it out, even if it were in the middle of the procession. – Fray Pedro de Royuela, Vicar of Carmen de Toledo.'

In response to this and to the advice of several of his counsellors, from both sides, the King sent Pazos, the President of the Council, and the Cardinal Archbishop of Toledo, who was related to Ana, to ask Ana and Pérez to make up the quarrel, to concede the reconciliation Mateo

Vázquez publicly declared he wanted. From the Princess he drew this haughty reply.

'Sir, (the Spanish is an abrupt *Señor)*

'Your Majesty has sent the Cardinal of Toledo to talk with me about the business concerning Antonio Pérez, so that I might try to subdue him (Pérez) – I have understood and dealt with the matter quite differently from the way in which you intended because for a man to be innocent after so much persecution, without honour or peace, was not something he could accept as just, nor could anyone reasonably persuade him that it was: but anything is possible in the service of Your Majesty. I'm sure Your Majesty can recall that I informed you in writing of what I have heard Mateo Vázquez and his men are saying – that those who entered my house fell from favour with Your Majesty. Since then I have heard that they have gone even further and are saying that Antonio Pérez killed Escovedo on my behalf and that he has so many obligations to my house that when I asked him to do it he had no choice. Since these people have gone so far and to such extremes in their daring and shamelessness Your Majesty as King and Knight is obliged to make an example of them that will be known wherever their audacities are known. If Your Majesty does not see matters in this way, but wants all authority to be lost from this house and the estates of my ancestors too, and the well-deserved favour of the Prince (her dead husband), if these are to be the thanks and recompense for his services, then . . . '

And so she goes on at some length, concluding:

'. . . so I say to Your Majesty that when I think of how different my husband's deserts are, and of the shamelessness of that Moorish Dog (Mateo Vázquez) Your Majesty has in your service, I am sometimes brought to the point of going out of my mind . . . '

Philip sent his confessor, Fray Diego de Chaves, to see her and inquire whether she had any proofs of her allegations against Vázquez. For answer she appealed to the

Cardinal-Archbishop of Toledo and to Philip's chaplain, Hernando del Castillo. They both supported her.

The quarrel was intensified when Pérez, who was at the time at the Escorial, sent his officer-of-state to Vázquez's house to fetch an official paper that was to be submitted to the King. Vázquez duly sent it, but also fastened to it another paper in his own handwriting full of denunciations and the insult that Pérez was of low caste. The indignant Pérez took this paper to Philip, entreating him to grant him satisfaction of his calumniator or to permit him to get it himself. Philip, always a master of equivocation, seemed to promise, but postponed it. 'Before proceeding against Mateo Vázquez'; he wrote, 'respecting that paper or libel, it would be well to despatch the various state papers he holds, which concern a great many people.' But in a subsequent letter he wrote: 'I have not had the courage to examine the findings of you know whom.'

Pérez replied: 'I see that having served my prince with what talents I have and despite the particular assurances he has given me, my evil genius is gaining the day. While everything succeeds for him, in spite of his numerous faults and his offences against a noble lady and a man who wanted to be useful and who, to be so, ventured to do what I have done.'

Nothing was done; Vázquez increased in favour and at last Pérez abandoned hope of retaining his influence and wrote to Philip: 'I release you from the promise you gave me that I should have satisfaction but I entreat Your Majesty to allow me to withdraw from the persecution of my enemies by retiring with your good graces as a testimony to my fidelity and as the only reward of my services.'

At this point Ana intervened again. She had begun to realise that nothing was likely to induce Philip to give up Vázquez and that her continued hostility would only harm herself and Pérez. Consequently she tried to persuade her lover to make peace with his rival. After all they had worked together without too much friction in the old days.

'But it is not a question of working together,' said Antonio. 'It is a matter of murder.'

'You have the letters?'

'Of course.'

'Which means that Philip cannot accuse you without condemning himself.'

'If it came to a trial, possibly. But why should he allow it to?'

'Because he cannot stop it,' Ana retorted. 'It's not a matter of State; it's a public scandal.'

Against his better judgment, Pérez allowed himself to be persuaded. On the scorching afternoon of Tuesday, 28 July 1579, during the week of festivities in honour of Spain's patron saint, St. James, Antonio promised Ana that he would see the King on the morrow for an official reconciliation with Vázquez. In the evening he went through his papers with the King in his office according to their usual custom, then left Philip to go through them again on his own, which was also usual. Philip used this time to discuss Pérez with Vázquez. At ten in the evening Pérez received a note from the King sending back some of the morning's papers, adding he would take a decision in the matter of the reconciliation before returning to the Escorial. No doubt this last note was meant to reassure Pérez, who was possibly already contemplating flight, for an hour later, at eleven o'clock, Alvaro García de Toledo, *alcalde* of the Court, came with an order from the King and arrested him. Pérez was taken to the *alcalde*'s house.

A little later, perhaps by chance, perhaps acting on information, Ana came to Pérez's house in the Plaza del Cordon and found the door closed. She sent in her *dueña de confianza* to find out what had happened and while she was waiting alone friends of Pérez arrived with news of his arrest. She hurried back to her own house and there, a few minutes later, a similar scene took place. Don Rodrigo Manuel, Captain of the King's Spanish Guard, was announced. Ana welcomed him with sarcasm, congratulating him on his 'fine taste in visiting her at such an hour on Pérez's business'. However, his orders allowed for no delay – indeed Philip himself, dressed as an ordinary citizen, watched it from the porch of Great St. Mary's opposite her mansion. When it was all over he returned to the palace and paced unhappily about his room until five in the morning. Then he sat down and wrote in his own hand to the Duke of Medina Sidonia who was Ana's son-in-law and the most considerable of her many powerful relations. He ended the letter: 'Because the Princess of Eboli not only did not facilitate the reconciliation between Pérez and Vázquez but actually impeded it, I have been obliged to order her arrest last night and to have her conveyed to the keep of the castle of Pinto. As you are her near relative I wished, as was proper, to inform you of it so that you should understand it properly and should know, moreover, that no one desires more than I do her tranquillity and freedom, the prosperity of her house and the establishment of her sons.'

This letter shows just how much Philip had achieved in the ten months leading up to the arrest; by playing off Mateo against Pérez and Ana he had procured immediate grounds for the arrest, grounds which would for a time silence the objections of the Pérez party and the nobility. It remains to ask why the arrest came when it did?

In December 1578 Philip had dismissed the Marquis of Los Vélez, Pérez's principal ally, and on 30 March 1597 he wrote to Cardinal Granvelle in Italy asking his old minister to return since he had 'the greatest need for his person'. At sixty-two years of age most of which had been spent in the service of Philip and his father the Emperor, the Cardinal was tired and reluctant; moreover he had been in semi-disgrace since his dismissal from the government of the Netherlands fifteen years before. But he came, and served his master faithfully though with increasing clash of wills between them until his death in 1586. However, he did not hurry, and he did not arrive until 28 July, the very day of Pérez's arrest. With the return of the Cardinal, Philip had no further need of Pérez.

The arrival of Granvelle gives us a reason for the exact date of the arrest, but hardly explains why it came so swiftly – it is almost as if the King had been waiting with indecent longing for the moment when he could effect something that had seemed a matter of urgency for many months, probably since March, when he first wrote to Granvelle; and although many thought the arrest was ordered because of Pérez's illicit liaison with Ana, and a few accepted what Philip chose to say on the matter – that it was because they had refused reconciliation with Mateo Vázquez – one man at least put in writing what he thought was the real reason. Pedro Núñez of Toledo, a follower of Mateo Vázquez, wrote on 25 August, just four weeks after the arrest: 'They have told me most secretly the real reason of these people's imprisonment was that the Jezebel (Ana) tried to marry her daughter to the Duke of Braganza's son and that for this purpose the Portuguese Gentleman* befriended her to the point of revealing the cipher and other little homely matters of the same sort.'

That the game was up in March is also indicated by the fact that Pérez in that month prepared to flee to Aragon but was dissuaded, and later sought a change of job to one that would take him to Italy, but was refused.

If Ana was really using Pérez in his capacity as Secretary for Portugal to negotiate a marriage between her daughter and the Duke of Braganza's son behind Philip's back, she was indeed lucky to survive eleven more years, however uncomfortably, unpoisoned and with her head on. These are the facts. On 4 August 1578, King Sebastian of Portugal died in battle at Alcázarquivir on a heroic and pointless

* To quote a Spanish historian: Pérez was known by this sobriquet 'because of his vanity and presumption – qualities traditionally ascribed by the Spanish to the Portuguese'.

crusade against the Moors leaving the old and infirm Cardinal Henry as King, and a disputed succession on the horizon as soon as the Cardinal died. In fact the Cardinal held on until 31 January 1580. The many claimants included various dukes of Italy and Savoy, and even Catherine de' Medici the Queen Mother of France – but the two best claims were undoubtedly those of Philip of Spain and Catherine Duchess of Braganza, both of whom were legitimate grandchildren of Emmanuel. In short, Ana, who was angered that lords should never be kings, was plotting to become presumptive Queen Mother of Portugal in direct competition with her sovereign.

Was there a peculiarly sharp irony in Philip's letter to Medina Sidonia – '. . . no one desires more than I do her tranquillity and freedom, the prosperity of her house, and the establishment of her sons . . .'? At all events Ana spent the next two years in close confinement, first in the Tower of Pinto, three leagues from Madrid, in a single circular room with a diameter of thirty feet, thirty feet above the ground with access by an outside staircase and walls three feet thick where, after roasting in what was left of the summer, she froze in winter. Yet only after falling seriously ill, was she moved to the Castle of San Torcaz; where there was a little more comfort but the confinement was as rigorous. There she stayed for another year in spite of appeals from all her powerful relations including the Duke of Medina Sidonia, the Archbishop of Toledo, and even the Cardinal King of Portugal himself. Only when Philip had securely united the throne of Portugal to that of Spain and ruled as sole monarch over the whole Peninsula was Ana allowed to return to Pastrana.

Throughout this first period of close confinement (a more severe one came later) every letter addressed to Philip on her behalf pleads solely on the grounds of the harshness of her punishment – no voice was raised to dispute its justice.

XVI
Who's In, Who's Out?

While Dukes, Archbishops, and even a Cardinal King pleaded with Philip on Ana's behalf, Pérez's chief, almost his only supporter was his wife, Doña Juana de Coëllo. As a contemporary said: 'she was often praised for heroism but never for her beauty'. Seduced by Pérez she gave birth to a son before she was married, and indeed he only married her under pressure from Philip and Ruy Gómez. She came from a noble family of Portuguese origin who had shown loyalty to Charles V against the Communeros and had been rewarded with favour*, and she brought with her to her belated marriage a large dowry; but her real treasure was her rectitude, her energy, her passion for and devotion to Antonio to whom she bore seven children in ten years. Her whole family was ruined by its connection with Pérez and she and her children were often in prison in the coming years – for a time even in the same Tower of Pinto that had held Ana, and she knew its grim walls for more than six months.

On her husband's arrest she went straight to Philip and found him apparently full of concern. He overwhelmed her with assurance of his affection for her husband. He explained, almost defensively, why, as an example to others,

* Pérez later blamed the hatred and prejudice of Barajas, who was descended from Communeros, on this connection. There may be something in this – anyone who knows Spain will not be surprised at feuds, dating from a civil war, lasting two or three generations.

it was necessary that there should be no rift between his counsellors. Now that Pérez had given his word that he would be reconciled with Vázquez there was no need for further detention. He would soon be at home with his family.

Juana thanked him quietly and remarked: 'The children miss him greatly.'

'If you can spare them, I could allow them to visit him at Don Alvaro's.'

'That, Your Majesty, would be most gracious.'

'And,' said Philip, 'my confessor shall visit him with my assurances.'

The confessor, when he carried out the commission, greeted Pérez: 'Do not fear, Don Antonio, I have come to assure you that your sickness is not mortal.'

'You have turned physician, then, Father?'

'No, but I have this on the word of the best doctor in Spain.' Then, answering Pérez's mute enquiry: 'Don Philip of Castile and Aragon.'

'You may tell him when next you see him that the best treatment is said by all experts to be freedom.'

In spite of the promises, freedom was not granted and Pérez found himself unable to bear his change of fortune. His loss of favour and the humiliation of his captivity combined with the impossibility of revenge and the dispiriting lassitude of inaction overwhelmed him. He fell ill. For this actual loss of health no physician could account and Philip relented to the extent of allowing him to be removed from the house of the *alcalde* and to occupy his own. Six days later the Captain of the Guard came to him in the King's name to demand the formal engagement – to renounce all enmity towards Mateo Vázquez and never to do him any harm or harm to his relations and friends. Pérez immediately gave his promise. But still release did not come. He was in fact detained eight months in close custody in his own house. At the end of that time the guards were indeed withdrawn, and he was permitted to go out for a walk and to attend Mass. He might also receive, but not pay, visits.

That summer Philip went to Portugal and from Lisbon sent such short answers to Pérez's continuing requests that the half-prisoner decided to ask his wife to visit the King once more. He also sent a monk, Father Rengipho, to support his pleas.

Philip, as soon as he heard that Doña Juana Coëllo was approaching Lisbon, ordered an *alcalde* to go and arrest her. This was done in the open day in the presence of a crowd of persons and it had such an effect on her, who was eight months pregnant, that she miscarried. The *alcalde* having questioned her, returned with her answers to the King who with a new inconsistency threw them into the fire without even reading them, and without saying a word, before the face of the stupefied *alcalde*, who left it on record that he 'felt a nervous shudder and silent dread' at the unaccountable scene. Could it have been that in Lisbon Philip had come across fresh evidence of Pérez's complicity in Ana's designs on the Portuguese succession?

The King, through the medium of Father Rengipho, requested Doña Juana to return home, assuring her, upon his word as a King and Knight, that as soon as he arrived back in Madrid he would give orders to release her husband completely.

He did nothing of the kind.

On the contrary, he instituted an inquiry into Pérez's conduct of his official duties. He appointed the President of the Council of Finance, Rodrigo Vázquez, as a secret investigator, suggesting that it seemed strange that one whose father had left him nothing should live in a style costing so much more than the emoluments of his office. This second Vázquez was no connection of Mateo's. He was, however, a Basque from Santander, as was Escovedo, and it is possible he was related to the murdered secretary, as Pérez later asserted. Rodrigo was pale, ascetic, and as a judge in

Granada and later on diplomatic missions to Portugal for Philip had earned a reputation for incorruptibility. It did not take him long to establish that Pérez took bribes on an enormous scale and, though Antonio was officially kept in ignorance of the investigation, the number and eminence of the witnesses – they included the major-domo of the Archduke Albert, the Count Fuensalida, the Archbishop of Seville and the Captain of the Royal Spanish Guard – and the gossip inevitably generated ensured that he became aware of it and he took counter measures in his own way.

Two of his intimates died suddenly. They were Pedro de la Era, his astrologer, and Rodrigo Morgado, his personal esquire who had carried so many messages between him and the Princess and witnessed many scenes in which Escovedo had been involved.

The astrologer's brother, Bartholomew, had no doubt that Pedro had been poisoned. He disclosed that the *alcalde* had forbidden the astrologer to leave Court without permission on account of his close connection with Pérez and that a few days later after he had dined with him, he had fallen ill from a certain powder which his host had given him pretending that it was a mineral bezoar, good for the stomach. Morgado's brother also believed that Rodrigo had been poisoned in the same way and for the same reason – that they might not reveal that he was Escovedo's murderer.

Soon the accomplices of the murder began to disappear in much the same way as those who had shared Pérez's secrets. Insausti did not long enjoy the rank of ensign that had been given him as a recompense for his participation in that murder. He died in Sicily a short time after his arrival there. Miguel Bosque, the brother of the ensign Antonio Enríquez, suffered the same fate in Catalonia. Antonio Enríquez, attributing his brother's death to Pérez and fearing that the same fate awaited himself, resolved, through animosity and the entreaties of Captain Don Pedro de Quintana, a near relation of Escovedo's, to reveal how and by whose order Don John's Secretary had been killed. On 23 June 1584 he wrote from Saragossa to the King to ask him for a safe conduct, undertaking to prove before a tribunal, and consenting to be hung by one foot as a traitor if he was unsuccessful, that Secretary Antonio Pérez had ordered the assassination of Secretary Escovedo. Having heard that the ensign named Chinchilla had arrived at Saragossa with designs against his person and a letter of recommendation for the Viceroy of Aragon he fled to Lérida whence he addressed another letter to Philip more pressing than the former. At the same time Captain Quintana wrote to the King: 'I very humbly beseech Your Majesty to deign, in consideration of the numerous services of the late Secretary Escovedo, to order that, in a space of time that may appear suitable to Your Majesty, proceedings be taken to give us the justice we expect against Antonio Pérez; since the crime is now unquestioned, I shall consider myself in this way sufficiently rewarded for the twenty years that I have served Your Majesty in war; for, not contented with what he has already done, the said Antonio Pérez wants also to put to death Don Pedro Escovedo and Ensign Enríquez in order that everything may remain buried in obscurity.' But Philip did not yet allow the investigation into Escovedo's death to be continued.

At the end of the inquiry for corruption, Philip decreed that Pérez should be 'confined and detained in any fortress it may please His Majesty to designate, for the space of two years or more, according to the King's pleasure; to be formally banished from court which he shall not approach within thirty leagues for ten years, and to be, for the same period, suspended from his functions; both penalties remaining, moreover, at the discretion of His Majesty and his successors. In the said banishment shall be included the time of his confinement in the fortress, and, in case of infraction, the penalty shall be doubled. Beside which, and within the space of the first nine days, he shall pay render and restore 12,224,793 maravids, in the form and manner following, namely 12,070,385 received by him and entrusted to him at Naples on the account of the lady Doña Ana de Mendoza, Princess of Eboli, save the right he may have to receive from the said Princess a certain tribute which he affirms to belong to him and to be imposed upon her for her estates and a variety of other matters including a sum of 7,371,098 maravids, all to be paid to the Chamber and Treasury of His Majesty.'

Pérez complained bitterly of this sentence without, however, justifying himself in regard to the facts. Three days before it was brought to him and to prevent him evading it, the two *alcaldes* presented themselves at the house where he was living half a prisoner and which was almost adjoining the church of St. Just. One of the *alcaldes* entered the study where his papers were kept in order to seize them and the other went up to the room where Pérez was in conversation with his wife. He told him of his instructions and arrested him.

Pérez immediately decided to place himself under the protection of ecclesiastical justice and sent one of his servants to consult the Cardinal of Toledo on the matter. While waiting his return, he entertained the *alcalde*. The Cardinal approved of his project and on his return the servant made Pérez understand so by a sign given in the presence of the unsuspecting *alcalde*. Pérez now told him that he would be back in a moment and stepped into the next room, the window of which looked out on the church. He jumped out of this window, which was only eight or nine feet from the ground, and took refuge in the church which was immediately shut. The *alcaldes* ran after him and had the doors burst open with a crowbar. They hunted a long time but finally discovered Pérez who had managed to squeeze himself under the actual roof. They dragged him out, covered with dust and cobwebs. In spite of the protestations and resistance of the priests they had him transported to their carriage in which he was shackled and handcuffed and taken to the church fortress of Turruegano.

The business did not end there. A long conflict ensued between the ecclesiastical and lay jurisdictions. The ecclesiastical arm denounced the two *alcaldes* for having violated the rights of the Church, and caused them to be successively condemned by a tribunal of the Vicar-General. They were ordered to replace Pérez in St. Just but Philip by the violence of his conduct made the ecclesiastical judges abandon their cause and eventually had the judgment pronounced against his *alcaldes* annulled in the Council of Castile.

In spite of the King's initial assurances, and the fact that for much of the time up to now Pérez had continued to carry out some of his secretarial duties, and been paid for them, it was now clear that his former master was, and would remain, an implacable enemy – but the key to what would have otherwise been a hopelessly brief and one-sided contest remained in Pérez's possession, that is, his secretarial papers. These certainly included those that implicated the King in Escovedo's death – but what else as well?

From Turruegano then Pérez through various mediators, the chief being the castellan Arrieta, set about negotiating the transfer of the documents, and while the negotiations proceeded he was not badly treated. Doña Juana and his children joined him there, he was allowed some of his income, and from the accounts that survive he did not live badly. Fish, partridge, oil, lambs' fry, chestnuts, eggs, apples, and wine were all paid for. Much was spent on candles and wood. But the apparent stalemate could not be maintained, and when he learnt through a friend that Arrieta had been instructed to poison him as soon as certain papers had been surrendered, he tried again to escape.

The attempt – to get to Aragon where the only way he could be tried was by the independent judiciary – was well-planned. Juan de Mesa, who had had a hand in murdering Escovedo, got as far as the fortress with two mules shod with their shoes reversed, but at the last moment they were betrayed and de Mesa was lucky to escape with his life.

As a result of this the conditions of imprisonment were swiftly altered. Pérez was strictly isolated and shackled in a small cell near the altar and the notorious Licentiate Torres de Avila, who had an unsavoury reputation as a skilled torturer, was made his new gaoler. His goods were confiscated and auctioned and worst of all Juana herself was now imprisoned and terribly threatened with perpetual confinement and a diet of a few ounces of bread a day if she did not give up the papers demanded. The King's confessor, Diego de Chaves, and Barajas, the new President of Castile, pursued her with entreaties and threats. No doubt she would have continued to refuse with heroic fortitude had not Pérez at last commanded her to give in in a note written in his own hand and signed with his blood.

Thus after a long resistance Pérez at last consented to put an end to his wife's captivity and to soften his own. Two trunks, locked and sealed, containing the papers so eagerly desired, were carried to the confessor, who, without opening them, immediately sent the keys to the King. This precious deposit was received with the more joy because the master thought he had deprived the servant at one stroke of the means of accusing him and of defending himself. But Pérez was as cunning as Philip and had managed, by the help of some of his faithful and intelligent servants, to abstract from the papers he delivered the most important for his defence and many notes in the King's handwriting.

Towards the end of the year 1587, after the papers had been given up, Pérez's captivity was less severe. After two years of rigorous imprisonment, he had fallen ill at Turruegano and Doña Juana obtained permission to have him removed to Madrid where for fourteen months he enjoyed again a sort of half freedom in one of the best houses of the town and received visits from the whole Court. They even granted him permission to attend Mass during Holy Week.

During this time Don Pedro Escovedo was, on his side, detained. He had been deprived of his post on the Council of Finances and put in prison, because he had complained of refusal of justice and was also suspected of intending Pérez's assassination.

The contradictory treatment practised towards Pérez astonished his enemies and Rodrigo Vázquez, questioned upon this subject, replied: 'I do not know what to say. Sometimes the King urges me on and lends me a hand; and then he withdraws it and stops me. I can make nothing of it and cannot fathom what kind of mysterious understanding there must be between the King and his subject.'

XVII
Confession Extorted

Rodrigo Vázquez may or may not have deserved his reputation for incorruptibility – what seems certain is that the remark just quoted is less than ingenuous for at that very moment a second trial was being secretly prepared, this time, at last, for murder. One supposes Philip, and Vázquez, were confident now that the papers delivered included all those that could embarrass the King.

The first sign that Pérez's newly won return to something like favour (though far short of his former glory) was spurious was the sudden arrest, ordered by Rodrigo, of his major-domo, Diego Martínez. Apparently he had been tricked from Aragon by a royal request to come and help with sorting and classifying his master's papers, and he came in good faith. At about the same time Pérez and his family were moved back to close arrest – this time in the fortress of Torrejón de Velasco. By November he was writing to the King in these terms: 'What has happened is that while Doña Juana was at Madrid to implore for my cure and life, the remedy for which depends on Your Majesty's compassion, the Alcalde Espinosa has arrested Diego Martínez who came to Madrid confidently like an innocent man. Although Doña Juana has had recourse to the President (Barajas) to claim Martínez as a person belonging to us, she has gained nothing for her pains.'

In February 1588 he wrote again, and in a different tone, one indeed which implied that Philip, as the accomplice and apparent instigator of the murder, would not want to see Martínez put to the question: 'I conjure Your Majesty to order your confessor to take immediate steps to prevent what seems about to happen. Since he is well acquainted with every part of this business, he better than anybody will advise what would be best to avoid consequences prejudicial to the prisoner (Martínez), to the service of God, and your own. A tribunal and severe judges sometimes go very far and it is not right to expose Martínez to this danger or to let him run this risk. I may venture to say that the remedy would be to restrain the judge and, especially, not to allow continual delay; because, if the adversaries produce a false accomplice who has safe conduct for his misdeeds, temporising will cause them to find others. Everything, on the contrary, may be prevented by despatch.'

But Philip, perhaps still confident that all the documentary evidence against him was in his hands, did nothing. He let Vázquez continue his investigation. The latter confronted, in the royal prison, Diego Martínez with the Ensign Enríquez to whom they had granted a safe conduct. Martínez treated Enríquez with scornful haughtiness calling him an ungrateful servant, a suborned witness, an odious wretch who had already committed crimes, as he was able to prove. Between the assertions of the one and the denials of the other, the judge was unable to decide. Another witness was necessary and Vázquez looked out for one.

Rubio the scullion had returned to Aragon, where also was the apothecary who had prepared the poisoned beverage for Escovedo. But the judges of the kingdom of Castile had no power in the kingdom of Aragon. Vázquez attempted to get the apothecary and the scullion brought before him and Pérez, informed of the danger, used all his ingenuity to prevent them appearing. He had them put in Juan de Mesa's care who managed to keep them back but did not any the less fear that by force or bribery they might be carried off and thus ruin all by their testimony.

Pérez wrote again to the King and requested him with repeated entreaties to put an end to these proceedings and restore him to favour. 'They have attempted several times to get possession of Juan Rubio and deliver him up to Escovedo. I have given myself a world of trouble, without annoying Your Majesty with it, to leave this Rubio closely watched and detained where he is by Juan de Mesa, a servant of mine, and a man of great abilities. God knows how uneasy I have been through ignorance of what had become of this Rubio, a scullion of whom Vázquez said he did not understand how it was that they had not got possession of him and why he did not appear as well as the other.'

Meanwhile Rodrigo Vázquez now decided that Enríquez's deposition, on its own, was sufficient to give a new character to the process, and he withdrew it from the obscurity of the mysterious inquiry of seven years' duration, and boldly implicated Pérez. On 21 August 1589 he ordered the prison where Pérez was, to be visited so that he might know whether it was safe and well guarded. When he was told that the apartments in which the prisoner was confined consisted of sixteen rooms so that the people in charge were unable to watch him carefully enough, that there were in the back part two doors that did not lock and by which people used to come and go during the night, and that Pérez had even been seen walking in the streets in broad daylight and unguarded, he requested the Count de Barajas to use greater precautions. The Count immediately ordered the doors and windows of the prison to be carefully shut and a greater number of guards to be placed about Pérez. Having taken these measures Vázquez interrogated Pérez twice about the murder of Escovedo, telling him of the heavy accusations which the deposition of his servant Enríquez had brought against him and his major-domo Martínez. Pérez denied everything and attempted with much assurance to put them on the wrong scent concerning the true cause of Escovedo's death.

Doña Juana de Coëllo was questioned but with no better result. On 25 August, after the second examination of Pérez, Vázquez pronounced the sentence confirming the crime, establishing the charges resulting from the preliminary proceedings, and granting them ten days to answer and defend themselves. Pedro Escovedo then brought his complaint in form against Pérez and Martínez. They chose their advocates, and at the end of the ten days they demanded and obtained eight more in which to produce their answer. At the same time Pérez, who was now in irons to make sure that he did not escape, furnished good security to have them taken off. On 7 September he produced six witnesses in his favour who declared that Secretary Escovedo and Secretary Antonio Pérez were intimate friends; that, at the time of the murder, Pérez was at Alcalá with the Marquis of los Velez; that he seemed much afflicted by it; and that they were convinced that Enríquez was a false and suborned witness because he had become the inseparable ally of the Escovedos. They added that Antonio Pérez, whose justification many important witnesses would have attested, was an eminent man and a good Christian, fearing God and injuring nobody. The same six witnesses attested the innocence of his major-domo Martínez.

Notwithstanding the ill-will of his judges and the hatred of his enemies, it was difficult legally to condemn Pérez against whom existed but one positive testimony, made in the spirit of revenge and opposed as being false. Accordingly, Vázquez devoted himself to a supplementary inquiry and tried harder than ever to secure the attendance of the apothecary from Aragon who had prepared the poison and of the ensign Juan Rubio. Pérez, profiting by his advantage and dreading the new delays so perilous to him, urgently demanded them to pronounce judgment and to set him at liberty.

During these transactions, Philip's confessor once more strangely interfered. At the very moment when the proofs were insufficient, he urged Pérez to complete them by a confession. In order to convince him he enunciated the theory of the innocence of murderers acting in obedience to kings. 'Knowing,' he said, 'the tribulation which you and yours have been so long suffering, I have asked myself whether I ought in Christian charity to give advice to one who does not ask it. I have at last resolved to do so; and thus I will tell you that since, in all truth, you have a peremptory excuse for the deed, when once averred, you ought to confess fully what they demand of you, and thus extricate yourself from the painful position in which you are; since that alone is and has been the cause of it. Let everyone afterwards answer for himself. May God preserve your Lordship many years in the health and tranquillity so necessary to your family.'

Pérez had more sense than to follow this advice which, under the appearance of interest, concealed a trap. He refused and grounded his conduct on the request of the King who had written to him: 'Do not trouble yourself about what your enemies are doing or what I allow them to do. I will not forsake you, and you can be assured that their animosity will be impotent against you, but you must take heed that they must not discover that the murder was committed by my order.'

Pérez therefore replied to the confessor after having taken counsel with the Cardinal of Toledo: 'To condemn myself thus in so serious a case would be acting against my conscience; especially when many innocent people would be compromised by my so doing; that to reveal what the King wished to keep secret would not be taking a prudent step; and lastly that in every respect it would be best to come to an understanding and arrangement with Escovedo.'

Escovedo had not in eleven years been able to prove the guilt of Pérez; and knew that if he did not succeed in getting him condemned he was himself exposed to a severe condemnation. He had mysteriously received a letter which probably Pérez had written to him. 'As I know that even if I were to tell you my name you would not know me it is useless for me to write it. It is sufficient for you to know that I am your friend, and as such, I will tell you not to annoy yourself by pursuing the business relative to your father, because you will gain nothing by it; and, if you had not been so blind, you might have seen that the King does not relish your prosecution, since it is upon that account that he has deprived you of your office; and, if you trespass too far, may God grant that you do not suffer the same fate as your father! I perform in this the duty of a friend. May God open your eyes! Your devoted friend who knows what he is saying.'

Consequently, at the very moment when the confessor was suggesting to Pérez and very likely suggesting it in the King's name, that he should confess everything, Pérez made use of the King's name to give Escovedo the hint to renounce his proceedings. This the latter consented to do in consideration of a sum of twenty thousand ducats. He thus sold his right of revenge.

On 28 September he gave in his abandonment of the prosecution in the presence of the clerk of the court. He required of Rodrigo Vázquez, as well as the court *alcaldes* and all other officers of justice, to cease to prosecute the cause, and also to restore Pérez and Martínez to liberty; declaring that he pardoned them in order to fulfil his duty towards God and to end this difference between them, having been entreated to do so by important persons.

He then removed himself from a situation where his presence could only mean danger to himself, from more than one source, and went on a pilgrimage to Guadalupe.

Philip's confessor approved of the reconciliation with Escovedo as a last resort. 'The other expedient which you mentioned to me,' said he, 'that of arranging the matter with Escovedo, is not bad; and it might be employed without making any mention of the King, who has an aversion for that man, both on his father's account and on his own.'

But Rodrigo Vázquez, whether out of scruples or hatred, remained unsatisfied. Instead of granting Pérez his freedom, which he claimed more earnestly than ever, Vázquez wrote to Philip that Pérez thought to get clear of the business by compromising it with Escovedo, but that the King 'ought to consider the many rumours that had been afloat respecting the order he had issued for the commission of this murder; that now it behoved his authority to appear, and to command Pérez to declare their reasons for inflicting this chastisement'. He added: 'They give Pérez to understand, Sire, that the murder is not proved by the process, though it is sufficiently so for me if I were judge; let Your Majesty write me therefore a note that I may show and in which you will say, "Tell Pérez that he knows how I ordered him to have Escovedo killed for motives that he knows right well and which it is expedient for my service that he now should declare." '

Hearing of this incredible project, the Cardinal of Toledo went to the King's confessor and said: 'Sir, either I am mad or this business is. If it be the King who ordered, and confesses he ordered, Pérez to put Escovedo to death, of what, and of what motives can they ask him to give an account? The more we reflect the more plainly we shall see that Pérez was not the judge in this act but only the Secretary and reporter of the despatches that came into his hands; after which he was the executor of what was ordered and entrusted as from friend to friend. And it is now, after twelve years, that he is asked to recapitulate the motives, after the seizure of his papers and the death of so many persons who might know and attest so many things. Bring to life five hundred dead people; restore him his papers unexamined and unread, and even then you will not have the right to do what you are doing.'

On 4 January 1590 Philip gave Rodrigo Vázquez a written order: 'You may tell Antonio Pérez, in my name, and, if necessary, by showing him this paper, that he knows well the knowledge I have of having commanded him to kill Escovedo, and the motives which he told me there were for so doing; and that, as it is important for my satisfaction and of my conscience that people should know whether those causes were sufficient or not, I order him to tell them in every particular, by giving *the proof of what he alleged against me in this manner*, of which, moreover, you are not ignorant, since I have communicated it to you particularly. When I see the answers he makes and the reasons he gives I shall order that such measures be taken about everything as will be most proper.'

Pérez had been extremely well guarded. His gaolers had been commanded to watch him narrowly, to let him speak to no one and not to speak to him themselves. When they showed Pérez the King's order, he answered that, saving the humble respect that he owed to the words of His Majesty, he had nothing more to say than what was contained in his former declarations; that he knew nothing about the murder of Escovedo, and had had nothing to do with it. At the same time he once more objected to Rodrigo Vázquez as a prejudiced and hostile judge.

Vázquez and a colleague, in accordance with the royal order, pressed Pérez on several different occasions – 25, 27 and 28 January and 1, 12, 20 and 21 February 1590 – to explain to them the motives for the death of Escovedo. Pérez simply answered that he would say nothing because he knew nothing.

They were resolved to have a confession from him. As they could not obtain it by fair means, they determined to get it from him by force. Rodrigo Vázquez on 21 February ordered the guards to bind him with a chain and put shackles on his feet. Pérez entreated the King humbly, but in vain, to order them to take off his irons which in his infirmity he was unable to bear. On 22 February, Vázquez went to the prison and ordered him once more to answer. Pérez still refused. He was then threatened with torture.

The official account ran: 'He protested against the use of torture to him, first, because he was of noble family and secondly because his life would be endangered, since he was already disabled by the effects of his eleven years' imprisonment. The two judges then ordered his irons and chain to be taken off, requiring him to take an oath to answer whatever he was asked. Upon his refusal the executioner stripped him of his garments and left him only his linen drawers. The executioner having left the room, Vázquez and his companion told him once more to obey the King's orders on pain of suffering torture by the rope. He repeated once more what he had already said. Immediately, the ladder and apparatus of torture having been brought, they crossed his arms one over the other and then proceeded to give him one twist of the rope. He uttered piercing cries, saying: "Jesus! I have nothing to declare; I shall die in torture; I will say nothing; I will die." This he repeated many times. By this time they had already given him four turns of the rope; and, the judges having returned to summon him to declare what they wanted of him, he said with many shrieks and exclamations: "I have nothing to say; they are breaking my arm. Good God! I have lost the use of one arm; the doctors know it well." He added with groans: "Ah! Lord, for the love of God! . . . They have crushed my hand, by the living God!" He said, moreover: "Señor Juan Gómez, you are a Christian; my brother, for the love of God, you are killing me, and I have nothing to declare." The judges replied again that he must make the declarations they wanted; but he only repeated: "Brother, you are killing me! Señor Juan Gómez, by Our Saviour's wounds, let them finish me with one blow! . . . Let them leave me, I will say whatever they will; for God's sake, brother, have compassion with me!" At the same time he entreated them to relieve him from the position in which he was placed, and to give him his clothes, saying he would speak. This did not happen until he had received eight turns of the rope.'

The declaration he then made admits, for the first time, that he not only gave the order for Escovedo's death, but that the idea was his in the first place. In answer to Philip's command that the motives for the murder should be made public ('as it is important for my satisfaction and of my conscience that people should know whether those causes were sufficient or not'), he said that Escovedo had been in touch with the Pope on Don John's behalf about an invasion of Britain behind Philip's back and that he had been plotting with the Guises; he asserted that papers had been shown to Philip and Los Vélez which said that Escovedo and Pérez would be lords of England; and finally that Don John had intended to invade Spain having taken the fortress of El Mogro in Santander. He said that Los Vélez had suggested poison for Escovedo.

None or little of this of course need be true; it simply recapitulated the original reasons Pérez had used to persuade Philip to accept Escovedo's murder. The judges said, as the King had before, that all must be proved – Pérez could only fall back on his earlier excuses: the King now had the papers. Los Vélez and the other witnesses were dead.

Thus he condemned himself. In effect he admitted there was no *proof* that Escovedo and Don John had been plotting against the King; he agreed (always, be it remembered, under torture) that the order for the murder had come from him and not from Philip; that Philip's only fault was that he had let a *fait accompli* go by.

On the next day the devoted Diego Martinez, who till then had been silent, saw that his master had confessed everything and thought himself no longer obliged to keep silence. He confirmed by a circumstantial declaration the account which Endríquez had given of the death of Escovedo.

Pérez's downfall was too great to allow the continuance of any envy of his position. The Court was surprised and frightened to see torture used towards a man of such high rank, a minister and a favourite of the King. No one thought himself any longer safe from this barbarous 'justice'. They began too to see that the King and Pérez had participated in a deed for which one suffered the torture which the other commanded. They murmured openly about it at Court and one of the chief persons there even exclaimed with indignation: 'Treachery from a subject to a sovereign is common; but never was such treachery seen from a sovereign to a subject.' The Court preacher even said publicly in the Royal Chapel:'Men, after what are you running? Do you not see the peril in which you live? Have you not seen one yesterday at the pinnacle of fortune who is now at the torture? And do you not know why he has been tortured for so many years? What do you want then and what do you still hope for in looking for promotion?'

As for Pérez, he was attacked by a fever. And, worse, he clearly saw the fate that was in store for him – death after torture. He knew that Vázquez had told the King that, deprived of his papers, he could no longer clear himself. Vázquez examined new witnesses and directed his inquiries to prove more and more that Escovedo's murder had its roots in the intimacy between Pérez and the Princess of Eboli; and he proceeded to implicate Pérez also in the death of the astrologer and of Morgado.

In this extremity, Pérez thought more than ever of escaping what was obviously in store for him, but he could not see how. Both his arms were crippled; he was ill, alone, and closely guarded. On 27 February, he begged to be allowed his usual servants to take care of him during his illness. His doctor confirmed that he was 'in a burning fever, in danger of his life if they did not give him care'. On 2 March, they authorised a page, chosen by his wife, to wait on him in prison on condition he should never go out or speak to anybody. As his illness seemed to increase Juana, about the middle of March, requested that they would permit her and her children to visit him so that he might not die without seeing them. At first she met with a refusal.

At High Mass at the Dominican church she had actually thrown herself before the King's confessor, demanding in the name of the Blessed Sacrament that the priest should refuse to absolve the King unless he set Pérez free. She continued to make entreaties to visit him and eventually, at the beginning of April, was allowed to join him.

Pérez seemed more than ever worn out by suffering but on the evening of Wednesday in Holy Week, 20 April, at about nine o'clock, having put on a dress and cloak belonging to his wife he managed, so disguised, to escape. One of his friends met him outside. And a little further on Gil de Mesa, the ensign, was waiting with horses to escape to Aragon. They rode thirty Spanish leagues without stopping and at last set foot in Aragon where he could rely on the justice of a court prepared to defy the King.

Not far along their way, at Alcalá and again at Guadalajara, they passed roads that led to Pastrana. Pérez can hardly have expected to return, at least not in the lifetime of his royal master, and we must suppose he looked down those byways with nostalgia, regret even, for the bright years of a youth spent in the household of Ruy Gómez, Duke of Pastrana and Prince of Eboli. And he must have spared a thought for the Princess who was now a prisoner there – for he had written to her after their first imprisonment and possibly visited her during the intervals when he had been allowed some freedom – yet it seems likely his feelings towards her had by now turned bitter: later in exile he said, 'A Lady harmed and ruined me,' and, 'There is no lion wilder, no wild beast crueller than a lovely lady. Such a one must be fled from,' and, 'I want no more suits with Princesses.'

Within a month she had cause too to cry out against him – for one consequence of his flight was that the conditions of her imprisonment were rendered intolerably harsh and her premature death was thus hastened.

XVIII
The Fueros of Aragon

Don Juan de Luna, Baron of Purroy, had been an old friend of Gonzalo Pérez, Antonio's father. He still lived in Aragon and survived the catastrophic events that followed the return of Gonzalo's son as a fugitive – not *from* but *to* justice – survived long enough to leave some record of them.

'Pérez,' he said, 'turned up like a spark in a pile of tinder.'

The situation in Aragon was complex, though it has been simplified often enough by historians with axes to grind or hobby-horses to ride: simple if you think the rise of the nation-state has been a good thing and approve of centralisation round a powerful bureaucracy – then Philip is a Promethean hero, Aragon and its nobility an out-worn order that had to be destroyed; simple if you believe in local rights, regionalism, self-determination – then Philip is a ruthless tyrant backed by a faceless machine and Aragon stands for human needs, the individual and so on.

But there were other issues too. Many of the rights the Aragonese nobles clung to and which were enshrined in their *fueros* were rights of vassalage which allowed them, when they were so minded, to keep their peasants, for the most part Moriscoes, in a state close to slavery; on the other hand they could *favour* their Moriscoe serfs at the expense of the 'free' old Christians who were mostly pastoral and lived in the Pyrenees. The stresses arising in this divided society had already led to revolts from both Moriscoes and shepherds, and in some parts of Aragon civil war had become endemic.

The largest barony in Aragon was that of Ribagorza, which included seventeen towns and two hundred and sixteen villages, and was in the hands of the Duke of Villahermosa who would willingly have accepted compensation for its incorporation into the Royal Domain if a figure could have been agreed, for it was in this domain that rebellion remained open and continuous.

The other aspect of the *fueros* to irritate Philip so deeply was of course the judicial system which he, like Isabella the Catholic a century before when the crowns were first united, had sworn to uphold and defend. Again, this was no simple matter, but, briefly, the part which concerns Pérez was the privilege of *manifestación* whereby anybody of Aragonese parentage could claim, once on the soil of Aragon, the right of protection by the *Justiciar* of Aragon from summary arrest by royal officials, and the right to be tried and sentenced by the Court of the *Justiciar*. Prisoners claiming this right were called *manifestados* and were kept in a special prison from whose windows they could be seen so that the populace could remain satisfied that nothing had been done to them without trial. It was as a *manifestado* that Pérez hoped to arrive in Zaragoza.

Three years earlier, Philip had decided to appoint a neutral viceroy (there had never been a viceroy before), the Marquis of Almenara. In 1588 Almenara had come to Zaragoza and submitted the possibility of his appointment to the Court of the *Justiciar.* Surprisingly the Court had found that the creation of a viceroy was not illegal. However, the nobility, the clergy, and the inhabitants of Zaragoza saw this as yet one more Castilian attempt to whittle away the *fueros*; and, when it was reported, in spring of 1590, that Almenara was about to return with increased powers that suggested he would shortly be invested as viceroy, an eruption of popular feeling, in the major city at least, was already a probability. Such was Luna's 'pile of tinder' that Pérez was to ignite.

Pérez halted for several days at Calatayud on the border between the two kingdoms and from there, no doubt encouraged by reports from Madrid that feeling was on his side (many were shocked that one of his position should have been tortured and even the King's jester Uncle Martin said to Philip: 'Why be angry at Pérez's escape – everyone is so happy at it, he must be innocent; rejoice, therefore, like other people!') penned a long and conciliatory letter to the King asking only 'for some corner' to live in in peace with his wife and children.

But Philip had already had Juana and the children arrested – on Maundy Thursday 'the day when it was usual to pardon the very worst of criminals' as Antonio later wrote, and confined them, with Juana once more in her eighth month, in the public gaol – 'persons whose condition, sex, age, and crimes were very deserving of such a dwelling' the exile was to add with high sarcasm.

Deserving, no – but the imprisoned wife and children remained for many years Philip's surety of Pérez's behaviour abroad: he never, in writing, accused Philip of any of the crimes of state he knew of save only complicity in the death of Escovedo which had always been the keystone of his defence; or in writing revealed any of the other state secrets he obviously knew.

Pérez nearly overstayed his time in Calatayud. Hardly had he been there ten hours than an order arrived to seize him dead or alive. He was forced, with his companion Mayorini, to seek sanctuary again, this time in a Dominican convent; however, Gil de Mesa, Juan de Mesa's son, successfully invoked the privilege of *manifestación* and Don Juan de Luna, backed by fifty arquebusiers and the people of the town, escorted him out of the Convent and to the Charter Prison at Zaragoza.

Philip now had to observe Aragon law and he started by

lodging a complaint in form that Pérez had murdered Escovedo falsely making use of the King's name to do so, divulged secrets of state, and escaped from prison. But Pérez was again in possession of the magic papers he had always contrived to keep from Philip – whether they had gone secretly to Aragon before him, or whether he had brought them with him, is uncertain; some had possibly been copied (one remembers that expensive use of candles at Turruegano) and the copies only given up to Philip; and so in May he was able to write to the King's confessor, Diego de Chaves, 'Let Your Paternity consider whether it be proper the King's secrets should be brought before a tribunal'; and in June he showed his papers to one Philip, the Prior of Gator, and sent him to the King in person.

'His Majesty,' he said to the Prior, 'must learn from you what pledges I possess for my acquittal in order to judge whether it be proper to produce them in court thus compromising many considerable persons, staggering the affection of his own subjects, scandalising the whole world, and raising doubts even of his prudence and piety.' He went on to say that God in his mercy and justice had enabled him to hold back these papers to justify himself and even to 'set in a glorious light the loyalty of my services' and 'my meritorious fidelity'. Yet he would prefer not to have to use them for always he was ready 'to sacrifice myself to the welfare of the King's service, to the honour of his affairs, and to the opinion which is entertained of him by the world'. Or, to put it another way, if the King withdrew his charges, guaranteed his safety and that of his family, a deal could be made.

The King countered with a sentence published in Madrid above the names of Rodrigo Vázquez and Juan Gómez that condemned Antonio Pérez, late secretary of the *Despacho Universal*, to die by the gibbet after being dragged through the streets of the town, to have his head cut off with an iron and steel knife and exposed in a public place – but this had no effect on the judges of Aragon. The trial in Zaragoza continued unchecked and Pérez drew up a *memorial* of his case. Philip, now uneasy, wrote to the judge for a resumé of this document and the judge's personal opinion of it. The reply indicated that Pérez would be acquitted on all three counts.

The King withdrew his charges but kept open the right 'safe and free . . . to be able, before any other tribunal, to bring him to an account and have satisfaction for the said accusation, and sue him at any time for the said offences', His withdrawal rallied opinion to his side, and indeed many of the Aragonese nobles were already frightened by the extent to which they were drawing royal disfavour on themselves, and a new prosecution quickly followed, this time accusing Pérez of poisoning the astrologer Pedro de la Era and Rodrigo de Morgado, but it was asserted in the declaration of the physicians that both had died naturally. Next, the Marquis of Almenara tried to institute a tribunal like the one Pérez had been condemned by in 1585 for corruption, but this failed since Pérez could show he had never been an officer of the King in Aragon; moreover, he could not be condemned twice for the same crimes. Having survived charges of murder, treason, escape, poisoning, and corruption Pérez demanded his freedom, or at least to be let out on bail.

The one remaining weapon the King could use against Pérez was the Inquisition. It had the advantage that its operations were outside the privilege of *manifestación*, but the disadvantage that up till then no one had bothered to record whether Pérez had done anything which the Holy Office could construe as heresy. However, obliging courtiers, understanding what was required of them, volunteered evidence.

Some had heard Pérez say: 'If God put any obstacle in my way I would cut off His nose for having permitted the King to prove himself so disloyal a knight to me.' This, the Holy Office declared, savoured of the heresy of the Vaudois, who pretend God the Father (and clearly Pérez here was referring to the First Person of the Trinity) is corporeal and has human members. On another occasion it was remembered that the accused had said, 'I am quite at the end of my belief. It seems that God sleeps in the business that concerns me . . .' Clearly this was offensive to pious ears, implying as it did that Pérez, who had been judicially tortured and condemned to death, could be innocent and without reproach. 'God sleeps. God is asleep! All we have been told about the existence of God must only be a joke; there cannot be a God,' cried Pérez on hearing of the suffering of his wife and children. This proposition, in as much as it says God is asleep, is suspected of heresy. Scriptures and the Catholic Church teach us of God's unremitting care of human affairs; as for the rest, he who doubts in a matter of Faith is an infidel.

On 24 May 1591 the Inquisitors made their pronouncement: 'We, the Inquisitors especially delegated by Apostolic authority against heretical perversity and apostasy in this kingdom of Aragon . . . command Alonso de Herrera, Alguazil of this Holy Office . . . to seize the body of Antonio Pérez in whatever place it may be, whether church, monastery . . . or privileged place . . . to conduct him carefully and safely into the prisons of this Holy Office . . .'

On this instruction Almenara sent his men for Pérez and Mayorini. At first everything went as planned. They took an inventory of Pérez's effects – among which were a copy of the *fueros*, a portrait of his father, and an image of Our Lady of Sorrows – and placed him and Mayorini in a carriage for the short journey to the prison of the Holy Office, the Aljaferia. But then the people of Zaragoza took a hand.

A tocsin sounded, an armed multitude assembled shouting 'Liberty for ever!' 'Death to the traitors!' and the most inflammatory cry of all went up '*Contra fuero!*' While some attacked Almenara's mansion where the unfortunate Marquis was caught, abused, and injured – he died a fortnight later – the main mob assembled in front of the Aljaferia and with shouts of 'Castilian hypocrites set the prisoners free or you shall be burned as you burn others', demanded Pérez's release.

Although the Inquisitors remained firm in the most important particular – they refused to renounce their prosecution – they gave up their prisoner on condition he was returned to the prison of the *Manifestados*. The crowd followed, pressing round him and crying out: 'Señor Pérez, when you are in prison show yourself three times a day at the window, that we may see you and thus prevent them from violating our liberties and *fueros*.' As soon as Pérez was back under the guard of the *Justiciar Mayor* the insurrection ceased.

Philip was not yet ready to crush the Aragonese. He was at war with the English, the Turks, the Dutch United Provinces, and coping with armed incursions from Portugal, besides being involved in the armed conflict between Henry IV and the Catholic League. For the time being a show of clemency was expedient, provided the Aragonese showed a willingness to return to obedience. On their side the Aragonese nobility had undoubtedly had a fright and were eager to negotiate a compromise and stave off the wrath of their monarch. After many debates and much irresolution a convocation of thirteen consulting judges decided that while the Holy Office could not annul the right of *manifestación*, it could suspend it – a face-saving formula Philip for the time being accepted.

Meanwhile Don Pedro Pacheco, the Inquisitor, instituted a secret inquiry into the riot, which, amongst other things, uncovered various examples of Pérez's arrogance: he had commissioned designs for his 'housings' (the ceremonial caparison of his horse) which demonstrated allegorically all the injustices he had suffered from the King; he had vowed to make an offering of a huge silver lamp to our Lady of the

Pillar (the patroness of Zaragoza Cathedral) the inscription of which would describe his escape from a barbarous people and the wrath of a wicked king. Irritating though these were, more serious by far were his open recommendations that Aragon should declare itself a republic like Genoa or Venice, or put itself under the protection of Henry IV.

One can thus easily appreciate how the legal decision that the Holy Office could suspend the right of a *manifestado* came as a terrible shock to Antonio. Advised to submit to rearrest he declared heatedly: 'None of those who love me can seriously give me this counsel. Molina (one of the Inquisitors) would willingly shed his own blood to drink mine. It is not justice I fear but the prejudice of the judges, who have ever persecuted me.' He produced *pasquinades* warning the populace of the danger to the *fueros* if he was taken back to the Aljaferia; he tried to escape by filing the iron bars in his prison for three nights with a file brought by friends in a basket of fruit, but one of these friends was false and the attempt was discovered.

The preparations for his removal, fixed for 24 September, were much more thorough this time and had the support of the Justices, most of the nobility and the senior clergy. All was to be done with due ceremony and unquestionable legality, backed by large bodies of troops, but the ordinary citizens of Zaragoza were still behind Pérez and in Gil de Mesa and Francisco de Ayerbe he had two friends with the skill and determination needed to marshal this support. Gil with shield and sword, Francisco with musket and the support of fifty or so armed *lacayos* skilfully outmanoeuvred the soldiers; the building where the *Justiciar Mayor* was sitting to make out the order was fired and he and his staff had to break down the back walls to get out, the lieutenant of the prison and his men had to flee over the roofs of the houses. A cheering crowd followed Pérez with his friends for nearly three miles beyond the city boundaries before allowing him to go into the mountains with Gil de Mesa to await a favourable chance to cross into France.

Although the Aragonese authorities had done their best to follow the King's wishes Philip now felt able to use this second riot as an excuse to foment the quarrel, since it suited his purpose to do so. Very probably he cynically recalled a saying of his great-grandmother Isabella whose marriage to Ferdinand of Aragon had first united the crowns: 'My greatest desire is that the Aragonese might revolt and thus give me the chance of destroying their *fueros*'; at all events by the middle of October a large Castilian army was concentrating at Agreda on the border under Alonso de Vargas, who, since he was not high-born, had no ties at all with the Aragonese nobility.

The latter countered on 27 October by objecting to this army and invoking ancient treaties with Valencia and Catalonia; at the same time, they mounted an intensive search for Pérez, whose head they realised might now save them, and he was forced to return in disguise from the mountains and hide in the house of Don Martín de Lanuza, the brother of the *Justiciar Mayor*. On 2 November Philip answered in terms of careful threat. The army was for France, but if on its way through Aragon it found crimes to be remedied it would do so. He also said he wanted to promote Aragon's welfare by the maintenance of peace in the Kingdom and 'as I have no other desire those who do not conform to my wishes will commit a real offence and incur a heavy responsibility.'

A new convocation of the judges declared by twelve votes to one that they were obliged by the *fueros* to arm. Don Juan de Lanuza, the last *Justiciar* they were to have, was made commander and his brother Don Martín a colonel; but the resistance was limited to Zaragoza – no Catalans or Valencians came, only two other towns in Aragon offered support. The Zaragozans warned Vargas he was liable to incur the death penalty if he invaded; his laconic reply – that he would justify his right to invade once he was in Zaragoza – was backed by 10,000 foot, 1,500 cavalry and arquebusiers on horseback, with artillery.

Against such an army Lanuza could do nothing but retire with his much smaller force to a nearby fortress. On 12 November Vargas entered Zaragoza; his troops marched as if occupying a captured city – with colours flying, tambours and fifes playing, pikes and halberds at the ready, and the slow matches of the arquebusiers alight. Antonio Pérez did not stay to see the sight. With Gil de Mesa and Francisco de Ayerbe he had left the day before, again making for the mountains.

For a month uneasy peace reigned in Zaragoza while Philip deliberated; then vengeance fell, ruthlessly, inexorably. On 19 December the leaders were arrested. On 20 December Don Juan de Lanuza, whose statue the Aragonese were not allowed to erect until 1907, was beheaded without trial. 'No one can judge me or condemn me,' said Don Juan, 'but the whole Cortes, the King, and the kingdom.' However, all that was needed was a slip of paper in the King's handwriting which read: 'You shall arrest Don Juan de Lanuza, Justiciar of Aragon, and cut off his head. I must hear of his death as soon as his arrest.'

On 24 December the King marked the Season of the Nativity with an amnesty. It was more like a proscription for it excluded all clergy involved in the rising – they were handed over to the Inquisition; the twelve consulting judges who had voted for the legality of resistance; all ensigns who had carried a banner for Aragon; and 119 named persons. Even the city's official hangman was executed by his assistant. Pérez – branded falsely as the grandson of a converted Jew later burnt for apostasy – headed the list. He was burnt, in effigy, the following October for heresy and treachery. Seventy-nine others were less fortunate and suffered in deed; moreover, their descendants in the male line were barred from holding any office and reduced to the level of peasants with no right to go on horseback, bear arms or wear jewellery – in perpetuity.

The Duke of Villahermosa and the Count of Aranda were imprisoned, and poisoned. They were the last of the old Eboli party to have held important office or exerted influence.

Philip abrogated to the monarchy all the duties and privileges of the justices, abolished the rights of citizens, and destroyed the *fueros* of Aragon.

XIX
Behind the Barrier

As one might expect of a man who loved gaiety, colour, show, and drama, Antonio Pérez was an *aficionado*. 'When I saw the bull's horns,' he later said, 'there was nothing for it but to make the final leap behind the barrier.' However, he was referring not to the *barrera* of the bull-ring, but to the Pyrenees.

In fact his leap was not quite so sudden as this suggests – no doubt he lingered in Spain for over a fortnight on account partly of the time of year and the state of the passes, and partly to see how things would turn out. He put it differently: 'I was like a dog of a faithful nature who, though beaten and ill-treated by his master and household, is loth to quit the walls of his dwelling.' After a week in 'rocks and caverns' he arrived in the mountain fortress of Lanuza near Sallent, the family home of the doomed *Justiciar*; he was accompanied by Don Martín and Gil de Mesa.

On 18 November he sent Gil over the pass ahead of him to Princess Catherine of Bourbon, sister of Henry of Navarre, now Henry IV of France and Philip's enemy. Henry had left his sister in Pau to look after his first, Béarnaise, kingdom. Gil carried the following letter: 'Most serene Lady, Antonio Pérez presents himself to Your Highness by means of this letter and the person who brings it. Madam, as there cannot be on earth any place so secluded and retired but the fame of my persecutions and adventures must have reached it, the knowledge of them will have penetrated into regions as exalted as those where your Highness resides. These persecutions are such and of such long duration, that they have reduced me to the most imperious and absolute necessity for my natural defence and preservation to seek a port where I may save my person and shelter myself from that tempestuous sea of troubles which, as is notorious to the whole world, the passion of certain ministers has raised against me with so much fury for so many years; a sufficient reason, Madam, to believe that I have been, like a millstone, proof against the hammer and every possible shock. I entreat your Highness to give me your protection and safe-conduct to enable me to arrive at the end which I pursue; or, should your Highness prefer, to grant me your support and a guide in order to be able to pass over in all safety to some other prince from whom I may receive the same benefit. Your Highness will thereby do an act worthy of your grandeur.'

Pérez and Don Martín left Sallent on 23 November, knowing a detachment of Vargas's army under the Baron Pinilla was only a day away, and arrived in Pau on the 26th after a dreadful journey through deep snow over a pass nearly six thousand feet high. Pérez wore a shepherd's coat – perhaps as disguise, but certainly against the weather – which he affected for some time after saying he was tired of courtier's clothes and afraid to wear them.

Catherine treated him well – some said too well – and gave him a room in the Mint Tower of the Château-Palace of Pau, a room hung with tapestries from the collection that can still be seen there, a silk bed, and a good fire. She even supported a disastrous expedition back into Aragon led by Gil de Mesa and Martín de Lanuza whose failure led the Protestant worthies of Pau to demand Pérez's impeachment. Catherine appeased them by announcing that Pérez was under arrest in his tower but without materially altering the conditions he lived under.

These were not the only problems to trouble the exile's

repose. First Philip tried to entice him back with promises regarding his wife and children. Martín de Lanuza, acting as intermediary, was arrested as soon as he set foot in Spain and was lucky to escape with his life. Then there was the first of several attempts to murder him: the first but surely the most extraordinary. Here is how Pérez described it, referring to himself in the third person.

'When Pérez was at Pau, they went so far as to try to make use of a lady of that country, who lacked neither beauty, gallantry, nor distinction; a notable woman, an Amazon and a huntress; riding, as they say, up hill and down dale. One would have thought they wanted to put to death some new Samson. In short, they offered her ten thousand crowns and six Spanish horses to come to Pau and form an intimacy with Pérez; and, after having charmed him by her beauty, to invite and entice him to her house, in order, some fine evening, to deliver him up or allow him to be carried off in a hunting party. The lady, either being importuned or desirous, from a curiosity natural to her sex, to know a man whom authority and his persecutors considered of so much consequence, or, lastly, for the purpose of warning the victim herself, feigned, as the sequel makes us believe, to accept the commission. She travelled to Pau and made acquaintance with Pérez. She visited him at his house. Messengers and love-letters flew about like hail. There were several parties of pleasure; but, in the end, the good disposition of the lady and her attachment for Pérez, gained the victory over interest, that metal of base alloy, which defiles more than any act of love; so that she herself came and revealed to him the machinations from beginning to end, together with the offers made and all that had followed. She did much more. She offered him her house and the revenue attached to it, with such a warmth of affection (if we may judge of love by its demonstrations), that any sound mathematician would say there was between that lady and Pérez an astrological sympathy.'

One wonders if Pérez was enjoying this lady's company, sharing this astrological sympathy, when news of Ana's death came to Pau, for it was in February of that year she died at Pastrana after months of singularly wretched confinement. Did he reflect at all on his old mistress as he hunted through the lush spring pastures of Béarn with this lady? And if he did, did he think of her with affection and regret, or with hatred and resentment? Although they had corresponded and probably seen each other since their first arrest in 1579 they had almost certainly had no contact since 1585. In the seven intervening years Pérez had lost all hope of returning to favour, and had discovered a true and rare loyalty in his wife who now suffered, with his children, a confinement as harsh as Ana's. One suspects that his later declarations ('As a Lady harmed and ruined me . . .' and so on, quoted earlier) marked a softening in his attitude with the years rather than a hardening.

It was foreign to Pérez's nature to remain inactive; he required funds; moreover he had motive enough for action so be it provided some sort of revenge on his former master – and giving all the aid he could to Philip's two greatest enemies, Henry IV and Elizabeth of England, certainly did that. Trusting that Philip would stop short of actually murdering his wife and children and that nothing he could do would worsen or improve their lot, he wrote to Henry IV as early as December 1591 asking for the 'favour of his shelter and protection'.

Henry received him at Tours in the spring of 1593 though no doubt correspondence, useful to Henry, had passed between them meanwhile, and then almost immediately passed him on to Elizabeth of England with this letter: 'Madam, one of the agreeable incidents of my journey to Tours has been to see Sr. Antonio Pérez, with my sister, as I had told her to bring him to me, and to have known him by the conferences he has had with me, to be a person not less capable of the post he has held, than unworthy of the persecution which he suffers . . . I hope to be able to employ advantageously for my affairs the intelligence and good understanding he has of those that have passed through his hands; and, for this purpose, I have retained him in my service; but thinking, Madam, that you would be very glad to see him and confer with him, I have thought it meet that he should go and kiss your hands, on the occasion of this voyage of the Vîdame de Chartres, and have been willing to furnish him with the present, in order that you may be pleased to favour him so much the more willingly with your kind welcome and gracious audience, from which, I feel sure, you will derive satisfaction, and hear from him what you may turn to advantage; entreating you, after having heard him, to let him return to me in the company of the said Vîdame, whom I have very expressly recommended to take care of his person, and to bring him back to me in safety; which will be to employ him not less for what will concern your service, as far as you may judge proper, than for my own; putting both in equal consideration, and yours constantly above all things. Thereupon, humbly kissing your hands, I pray God, Madam, to have you in His most holy keeping. Your most affectionate brother and servant, Henry. At Chartres, this 29th March.'

In the summer of 1593 Pérez enjoyed his first visit to England, and stayed longer than Henry IV would have liked; indeed he seems to have created quite a stir in Elizabeth's court. He quickly allied himself to the rising Earl of Essex whose faction was already challenging the long-established Cecil party, and this was a natural alliance on grounds of policy as well as temperament and taste. Lord Burghley was blowing cold on further support for Henry who was now a Catholic ('Paris is worth a Mass') and seemed able to handle the Spanish without further aid; however, Essex saw continuing confrontation with Spain as a means of glory and influence, so naturally made much of Pérez, as also did his followers including particularly

Francis Bacon. The Queen, too, though the politic side of her nature inclined as it usually did to the Cecil view of things, was delighted with this mercurial, witty, indiscreet and occasionally melancholy man who could tell her all the details of Philip's various plots against her – or at any rate confirm what her torturers had already discovered – and she gave him a pension of £130.

Some of the amusement he offered the court was unwitting: his exaggerated, florid and no doubt occasionally inaccurate mastery of English provoked smiles at least: or so one would guess from a play performed at court in 1594 when the London theatres were closed and courtly fare was what was required of a rising dramatist, a play in which figures one *Don Adriano de Armado, a fantastical Spaniard at the court of the King of Navarre* –

> 'a refined traveller of Spain
> A man in all the world's new fashion planted
> That hath a mint of phrases in his brain;
> On whom the music of his own vain tongue
> Doth ravish like enchanting harmony.
> A man of complements – whom right and wrong
> Have chose as umpire of their mutiny . . .'

who would, moreover, entertain with tales of 'many a knight from tawny Spain'.*

There was no Love's Labour Lost between him and Francis Bacon's mother who wrote complaining to her other son Antony of 'that bloody Pérez who Francis keeps as a coach companion and bed companion, a proud, profane, and costly fellow'.

* This supplements the often-made identification of Armado with Sir Walter Raleigh (see, *inter alia*, the present author's *The Day Shakespeare Died*). The Armado of the 1598 quarto is probably an uneasy synthesis of two earlier versions – a Raleigh one, and a Pérez one, and combines the most dramatically interesting features of both.

He found time that summer to write the *Relaciones de Rafael Peregrino* which recounted his life and adventures with much art and was calculated to render his ungrateful and relentless persecutor still more odious and attract yet more benevolence and compassion to its author. He sent copies to everyone who was anyone, even Lord Burghley, with letters gracefully written and melancholy in spirit. One recalls Armado's first line: 'Boy, what sign is it when a man of great spirit grows melancholy?' and the fulsome flattery of his letter to Shakespeare's King of Navarre.

The letter with which he confided his book to the patronage of the Earl of Essex was at once touching and flattering: 'Raphael Peregrino,' said he, 'the author of this book, has charged me to present it to your Excellency. Your Excellency is obliged to protect him, since he recommends himself to you. He must know that he wants a godfather, since he chooses such as you. Perhaps he trusted to his name, knowing that your Excellency is the support of the pilgrims of fortune.'

The hatred of Philip for Pérez became, if possible, still greater with the publication of this book which was translated into Dutch so the insurgents might learn from Pérez's fate and that of the Aragonese what awaited them if they were conquered.

Philip endeavoured again to rid himself of the author, who had so denounced his perfidy and cruelty to all Europe. Two Irishmen received and accepted from Count de Fuentes, the governor of the Netherlands, the mission to kill him. Being seized, in London, with letters which implicated them, they were, upon their own confession, condemned to death; and their heads were fixed upon one of the city gates, near Saint Paul's. Philip sought moreover by underhand manoeuvring, which did not succeed, to excite the distrust of the English court against Pérez, who complained to Essex 'of those Pharaohs plotting in Egypt, that the Queen might look upon him with suspicion'.

XX
The Rope-Dancer Rests

In spite of this and other attempts Pérez's star, though waning, still shone for a few years yet, and its decline was slow, almost unnoticeable at first. On 20 January 1595, Henry declared war on Philip (previously he had fought him only as an ally of the Catholic League) and on 30 April he wrote to Pérez: 'I extremely desire to see you' and pleaded too with Elizabeth and Essex to release him. He needed Pérez's experience and knowledge of Philip. Unfortunately Pérez was incapable of leaving a simple and favourable situation to look after itself – he had to meddle, and he promised Elizabeth he would maintain a secret correspondence with her in her interests.

To begin with all went well. At Dieppe fifty horsemen met him to escort him to Rouen; in Paris he was given for a residence the mansion of one of the last Dukes to support the Catholic League, a pension of 4,000 crowns, and two soldiers as permanent guards. These last he needed – this time it was Baron Pinilla, he who had nearly caught him at Sallent, who undertook for 600 ducats to kill him. The Baron followed the Irish to prison, torture, confession, execution and dismemberment. But, one heavy cloud was news of the death of Martín de Lanuza – Pérez wept to hear it.

Henry's war with Philip was going badly – he lost Ardres and Calais and Philip was making ground in Picardy – and Pérez was useful not only as one who knew Philip's mind but also as a friend of the Essex party through whom he could intrigue for more support from Elizabeth. Yet Pérez was uneasy – perhaps court life could never be quite comfortable again – and suspicious when his pension went unpaid, though Henry was chronically short of cash and himself wore darned shirts and doublets out at elbow. Antonio thought of returning to England or moving on to Florence, Venice or Holland, in spite of reassurance from Henry: 'You shall live nowhere Antonio in greater security than with me, and I desire you not to leave me.'

Then a false report – one can guess whence it emanated – that his wife was dead reached him. He wrote to Essex: 'I have lost the companion of my sufferings, the comforter of my griefs, the rib, the half of my soul, I ought rather to say the entire soul of my body . . . she has gone from the prison of the living to the sepulchre of the dead, that last asylum of the wretched in this age and their safe retreat.' He contemplated entering Holy Orders and Henry even promised him the Bishopric of Bordeaux on its reversion, and he still found useful work for him. In 1596 Henry managed to tighten his alliance with Elizabeth by threatening a unilateral peace with Philip, and Pérez returned to England as part of the mission renegotiating the treaty; but he found Essex already gone on the Cadiz expedition and the Cecils cold and distant. Back in France he still felt insecure.

With his new alliance and English gold behind him Henry was ready to prosecute the war more energetically and he at last made Pérez a full counsellor with promises of a cardinal's hat if his wife was dead, if not then one for his son; 12,000 crowns in bishoprics; his present pension of 4,000 crowns continued; a gift of 2,000 crowns; and the promise that the restitution of his Spanish property would figure as a condition in any settlement with Spain. That was in January 1597; in September Henry retook Amiens, and Philip – seventy years of age, exhausted and ill – sued for peace. At the same time Pérez's secret correspondence with Elizabeth came to light – she wanted the war to continue – and that meant his ruin. He was barred from the Council and Henry went back on his promise to include the reinstatement of Antonio and his family in the terms of the settlement. The Peace of Vervins was concluded on 2 May 1598; Philip died four months later at 5 a.m. on 13 September.

A contemporary life of Philip describes his passing: 'Death would not destroy him without having made him aware that the princes and monarchs of the earth have as miserable and shameful way of leaving it as the poor. He was inundated with a foul *phitiriasis* accompanied by a whole swarm of lice; but present suffering did not cause him so much apprehension as his future fate; for when he conjured up the abyss of Divine Justice, and the account he had to give It of so many days, so many actions, so much blood shed in mere waste, he would rather have been born a poor shepherd than monarch of Spain.' The accuracy of this may be doubted – especially if the commonly attributed authorship is accepted; for if it is, then here Antonio Pérez has his last word on his old master. We do know that on the morning of his death Philip heard from his bed the choristers singing the early Mass in the chapel below. With this sound in his ears he suddenly opened his eyes and fixed them immovably on the crucifix.

Yet Philip in his death remained his foe for there was now no place left for Pérez in the councils of Philip's enemies. Henry remained cool, and the pension unpaid; by 1601 the pensioner complained not just of being in debt, but in debt even for three months' supply of bread. In 1604 things had gone so much from bad to worse that he threw up his place in France and went off to England simply on the chance of finding employment there since Philip III had begun to negotiate a settlement with James I: his plan was to win favour with the new Philip by using – abusing, some would say – his knowledge of the English court in the Spanish king's interest. James heard of this, and of his landing, and, tearing his beard (for he was given to histrionic display), said: 'I would rather leave England myself than allow Pérez to remain here.' Distrusted now by all, the ex-minister crawled back to France and begged to have the pension he had renounced restored. He begged in vain.

He was disappointed too in his hopes of a reconciliation with the Spanish Crown – high hopes they had been when he learnt that Don Francisco Gómez, Marquis of Denia and later Duke of Lerma, a relation of Juana who had actually visited him in prison, was now the new king's favourite and chief minister. But the Duke of Lerma actually wrote to Henry IV and asked why the French king kept enemies of Spain in his service and Henry replied, only too accurately, that since the Peace, Pérez had received nothing.

One consolation alone was allowed to him in his last years – the knowledge that his family had been released from prison, and at last his sons, but not Juana, were allowed to travel to visit him.

Poverty bit harder. He moved – from St. Lazare to Rue du Temple, to Faubourg St. Victoire, to Rue de la Cerisaie – to escape creditors, to be near people he hoped to beg favours from. In 1610, Henry IV was assassinated and hope flared briefly with the arrival of the Duke of Feria who came to negotiate a marriage between Louis XIII and the Infanta – but the Duke had no instructions concerning the sick and penniless exile. During this period, Antonio wrote to a friend about a fashionable acrobatic show in Paris 'in which everyone went to see a rope-dancer who made such steps and took such dangerous leaps . . . but I did not go', and he continued, speaking not of circuses but of the world of intrigue in which he had spent his life, 'for I have danced on the rope myself, and I have seen dancers fall to the ground with their limbs broken. I, who am speaking to you, broke my back at it and I shall not figure therein a second time – there is too much danger and I am afraid.'

In late autumn of 1611 he fell mortally ill and dictated his will to the ever faithful Gil de Mesa – there was little to bequeath except protestations of his innocence and fidelity, hopes for the rehabilitation of his family. This 'man of complements, whom right and wrong have chose as umpire of their mutiny' died on 3 November, aged seventy-two, and was buried in Les Célestins.

It took four more years before Doña Juana achieved the revocation of the sentence that had condemned him as a heretic and which continued to debar his family from all but the right to live. The act of reparation was made definitive on 6 June 1615 – only then were Antonio's children, the youngest of whom were now in their late twenties and the oldest over forty and who had spent most of their lives in prison, restored to their rank and rights as Spanish nobles.

XXI

The Princess A Nun!

Not the least remarkable of Ruy Gómez's achievements, one which must have taxed all his skill at statecraft, was a happy and stable marriage lasting fourteen years* with Ana de Mendoza y Cerda, Duchess of Pastrana. Her grief at his death – terrible in its sincerity as well as in its expression – and the ten children she bore him bear witness to it but the most striking proof of his influence over her is a negative one. Those fourteen years comprised the only period of her life when she did not act with an aristocratic disdain for convention, propriety and the feelings of others.

This sounds a harsh judgment, especially contrasted with the romantic view of her – her beauty enhanced by her patch, her taste for magnificence in a dowdy court, her scorn for people who were stuffy, or pretentious, but many of whom were worthy and one of whom was a saint who would not give in to her whims. Her capriciousness and high-handed meddling had brought disaster to many, including herself, though she bore her wretched end with real dignity.

After her arrest in July 1579, Doña Ana was first put in the tiny Tower of Pinto, an inhospitable, mean, and degrading prison. There she was allowed only two servants, but one of

* That is excluding the seven between the actual wedding when she was twelve and its consummation when she was eighteen. It was during this gap that she lost her eye and it would have been then, if ever, that she was Philip's mistress.

these was Bernadina Cavero, her then favourite dueña, who had once caused disorder in the Gómez household by introducing into it more than twenty dependants. Soon Bernadina was caught passing a note out between two plates, and was tortured to find out what else she knew. Had Ana contrived even here to forward her plot to become Queen-Mother of Portugal? It is little wonder that as the August heat gave way to the winter of the Castilian steppe, the Princess's health began to fail. Her appeals supported by kings and dukes fell at first on deaf ears; it is not until February 1580 that she was moved to the Fortress-Church of San Torcaz, which had been built as a prison for erring clerics.

Here there was some improvement – two rooms to live in rather than one, the armed guard kept at a more discreet distance, the replacement in May of a soldier as her custodian by Juan de Samaniego. But still she was not allowed to see her children, nor allowed any say in the running of her household, nor – not surprisingly – any communication with the outside world. Ana refused to recognise any amelioration and Philip wrote to Cardinal King Henry of Portugal: 'But she has begun to cry out for this change, though it is to her advantage, for she is like that in everything and wants nothing but as the fancy takes her, indulging in the greatest liberties and rages that I believe a woman of her quality has ever given vent to, and all this without showing any sign of mending.' One feels sympathy for Juan de Samaniego. He had been a trusted, loyal, confidential servant of the family all his life as a business agent, diplomat, and aide to the Prince. He acted in Spain for no less a person than Margaret of Parma, and later for her children the Farneses. His appointment was certainly approved by Ana's son-in-law Medina Sidonia – yet Ana objected: poor Juan was simply not good enough, after all he was . . . a servant.

She fell ill again and her illness was urged as a reason for her removal to Pastrana. Cardinal King Henry died; Philip invaded Portugal, was resisted, and did not feel secure on the Portuguese throne till Lisbon fell in August, when, as is the custom, amnesties were declared. When she discovered they did not include her, Ana's condition deteriorated. 'She was,' Samaniego wrote, 'very depressed' – as well she might be now her design on that throne through a prospective son-in-law could be seen as a harmless whim. 'She has colic pains and a very great nausea and vomiting. Doctor Falcos has bled her five times but now desists for he feels her too weak for more.'

At last, in February 1581, the move to Pastrana was allowed, and immediately her health improved, so much so that Samaniego felt constrained to write to Medina Sidonia on 3 April: 'From Pastrana it may be known that my Lady is so well that on the night of Holy Thursday she publicly made the Stations of the Cross which worried me in one way because His Majesty and his ministers will think the illness at San Torcaz was feigned. I think as much for my part and I fear they will believe that I help Her Excellency to play the "dead vixen"; but if they knew how she has been with me they would well understand that she hasn't bribed me.'

Poor Samaniego – clearly he was not the person to be Ana's custodian. Once in the familiar surroundings of Pastrana with a freer regimen she began to do just as she liked. She sent for a band of bagpipers and dancers who unfortunately ran into a procession of *disciplinantes* praying for rain – indeed there was continual dancing, music and entertainment. Pérez, accompanied by a band of *pistoleros*, apparently rode over to see her. But all this was nothing to the gang of bravoes or bully-boys she collected about her who clearly terrorised Samaniego and probably everyone else in Pastrana as well. Samaniego wrote to Mateo Vázquez about them, fearing they might be used against the Secretary; Mateo, under the direction of the King to whom of course he had run with the tale, wrote to Anibal Moles, Regent of the Council of Italy (two at least of the bravoes were from Calabria); Moles took a sworn deposition from Samaniego. Here is the story – pieced together from the correspondence and the deposition.

Samaniego's letter to Mateo, June 1581: 'The paper which came separately I passed on in confession with the priest Your Worship sent me. It seemed to him a very serious matter and one which ought to be looked into deeply because though in one way it seemed amusing, in another, considering the situation of *La Canela*,* it shouldn't be taken as a joke. What we determined on was to find out as much as we can about what is going on, as Your Worship suggested, and, since it is true that *La Canela* has us under threat and keeps some bully-boys on this island (i.e. Pastrana) for this purpose we should keep you informed through her confessor.' Clearly though Samaniego did not really believe that admonishment from her confessor would do, for he continues: '. . . perhaps the real remedy would be to tell Don Hernando (Philip's Chaplain and Court Preacher) who has always set out to act for her good and the good of her house.

'I have told you how on the island there are at least two bully-boys. One is the man who used to come here among the bodyguard of *Pimpollo* and is now officially book-keeper. (This was Antonio Enríquez, known as Guardian Angel, one of Escovedo's murderers. His presence in Pastrana would have terrified Mateo.) The other is a vassal of *La Canela* from Calabria who has been an outlaw all his life and is known throughout the province as *Aluchali*, after the great Turkish privateer, on account of his famous crimes and robberies. He has been condemned by justice to a thousand hangings without him once falling into their hands and now lives safely under the branches of *La Canela*. Although he serves as a lacquey he carries loaded pistols in

* *La Canela*, cinnamon, or 'lovely young thing' is Ana. *Pimpollo*, rosebud, or nice young lady (!) is Pérez.

the turn-overs of his boots. There is also another Calabrian vassal of *La Canela* who serves here as major-domo and is called Camilo. *La Canela* seems to be trying to persuade him to turn bully-boy. Finally I don't know if we can consider in the same band the long-standing President of Tournaments who is now *alcalde* . . .' He concludes this letter by saying that all have uttered threats against Mateo and others, and against himself.

Here is Anibal Moles to Mateo, Madrid 18 July 1581, describing the sort of person he takes Aluchali to be. After saying that the man would be at large as a result of an amnesty declared in Naples in 1579 he goes on: 'this kind of man is a plague and cannot last long in any place without falling into some crime or misdemeanour . . . I have no doubt that when they arrest him they will find him carrying a pistol because these men go *in aeternum* with one, and it is a common saying among them that their pistol is their soul and that they have no other . . .'

In his deposition Samaniego describes, in the third person, how Aluchali and Camilo arrived. 'While he (Samaniego) was in San Torcaz a short while before the Princess left for Pastrana two Calabrians, vassals of the Princess, arrived there dressed as pilgrims with short cloaks and staffs and said they had come from Sant'Yago after having served His Majesty in the Portuguese war . . . (Had Ana sent for them? It seems likely.) Aluchali is a man of low character with a fierce face and dark brown beard, aged about forty-five . . . and the other three bravoes threatened him (Samaniego) with the said Aluchali.'

One of these bravoes was dismissed by Ana apparently because he could claim to have killed only one man. With the remaining three she used to hold mock debates, as if they were members of the Cortes and she the Monarch, and what they would debate was how her various enemies should be severally dealt with – Mateo's name being frequently on the list. Aluchali would answer by taking out his pistols and firing them off; the others recommended bludgeons, kicking, beating and each would give his opinion following the form of the Cortes 'according to his conscience'. Then the Cortes would be dissolved for the day.

In spite of the terror this no doubt inspired in Ana's bureaucratic enemies a year passed before Philip acted, and then, typically, he seized on her disorderly way of life as an excuse for punishing her for other crimes which he did not want published. The fact is the secret tribunal into Pérez's conduct had made its first reports; Philip feared the scandal involved in punishing Pérez and Ana together, so on 27 August 1582 he wrote from Lisbon to Rodrigo Vázquez suggesting that they should move first against Ana, giving her disorderly life as the reason, and 'leave the Pérez business as it stands at the moment; the inquiry should continue and all the necessary investigations for it carried out in secret. We should begin with the Princess's punishment. This will be in the manner you suggested, agreed between yourself and Fray Diego (the King's confessor) which seemed very well considered and well-drawn up to me'.

Just over two months later the following ukase was delivered to Ana.

'The KING. Princess of Eboli. Cousin: Rightfully bearing in mind the many and good services performed for me by your husband Prince Ruy Gómez da Silva, and wishing to show favour to your children and take care of them, and this much being fitting to his memory, position and estate, I am giving different orders in what concerns his affairs and yours from those that previously existed. Since it is right that you should attend to your retreat in calm and peace but cannot properly do so with so many occupations and affairs, I have decided to exonerate you from your tutelage and guardianship over the Duke of Pastrana and his brothers and sisters and have named in your place to be tutor and guardian for the time I see fit, Pedro Palomino, native of Valladolid, being convinced of his good character and that he will act as is fitting in this matter; and to this end I have made him governor and judge over the estate investing him with my power as King and Sovereign Lord in as far as it should concern him. I wished to inform you of this so that you might know and I charge you that on hearing from the said Pedro Palomino what he will tell you on my behalf, you will do it and carry it out without protest, because you cannot do otherwise at the present time for it is imposed on you by God, myself, and for the good and benefit of your house and children. He has been informed how to deal with your personage and what treatment is befitting to it.

From Lisbon, 8 November, 1582. I, the King.'

Pedro Palomino did not last long and was replaced by Alonso del Castillo Villasante, Knight of the Order of Santiago. His full title was Governor, Supreme Judge and Administrator over the Estates of Pastrana which meant amongst much else that Ana's hereditary rights of vassalage were invested in him – which must have been bad news for Aluchali who disappeared. It was not long before he and Ana were not on speaking terms, though what the original cause of their quarrel was is not known, but from then on he was obliged to communicate with her through a scribe who witnessed and conveyed the messages of each to the other. No doubt both felt safer with everything on record. The scribe was Jerónimo Torrontero and the entire correspondence (if that is the right word) remains to this day in the archives of the Duke of Infantado.

Ana was now confined to the interior rooms of the main floor of the palace. Only two windows, both in the same room, looked out on to the outside world – on the market place where she could watch the Moriscoes from the Albaicín quarter come to barter fruit and cloth. Above the roofs the crest of a hill of olive trees could be seen. For company she had her daughter, also Ana, who like her father was patient and devoted, and four maids – Isabel

Mata, María La Calsa (who had been at San Torcaz), Gregoria Morales, and Mari Gómez. She was able to watch Mass through a grille that looked into the chapel and it was through this grille that messages penned by Torrontero were passed. Don Alonso kept the keys of the rooms and the only access to them was through a turn-gate protected by a further grille watched by guards and porters who dealt with the provision of supplies and the disposal of rubbish.

Grilles and turn-gates of this sort were the normal arrangement used in enclosed orders of nuns – such as Teresa of Avila's Barefoot Carmelites to which Ana had once aspired to belong.

For eight years she lived thus, and throughout them showed no sign of repentance or even resignation: the King, the Court, her relations and friends were bombarded with letters protesting her innocence and the barbarity and inhumanity of her gaolers; day by day she waged war with Don Alonso. Then, on 19 May 1590, following Pérez's escape to Aragon, a letter came from the King. Ana was now to be confined to one room and strong grilles and bars were to be placed over the windows and all other openings.

Ana now bolted her doors on the inside so the alterations could not be made, but on 22 May Don Alonso's workmen forced their way in.

Torrontero tells the story of those days: 'The Princess asked for evidence to be given of the fact that Her Ladyship and the said Doña Ana her daughter are indisposed and in bed, and that evidence should be given of the condition of their room at the time, and the said door was opened. A material curtain had been hung beyond it, and facing the entrance was the bed of the Princess, in which, I believe, were both the Princess and her daughter. I did not see them, but I heard them speak. In the room were two other beds which seemed to be those of the maids. The whole of the room was filled with these three beds.

'Don Alonso ordered all the officials involved in the said

work to enter Her Ladyship's room with all courtesy and respect and pass on through it to those which gave on to the inner courtyard with the necessary materials for the said alteration. They were to make as little noise as they could and carry out their orders without speaking or concerning themselves with anything but their business and perform this with diligence and care. They entered thus the furthest room that gives on to the kitchen entrance. Here they placed two grilles, one in the frame of the window and the other further within leaving a gap of about two feet more or less, and they went about removing the frames of the other windows to carry out the same alteration. And when twelve o'clock midday had struck, the said governor ordered the workmen to go out in case Her Ladyship wished to eat . . .

'Don Alonso ordered Miguel Ruiz and other officials to place in the opening of the room which gives on to the marketplace a grille in the middle of the window space; then a second grille was cast and fixed two feet inside the first. This second was made of interwoven iron threads in the form of a blind.

'Next day Mari Gómez, a servant of Her Ladyship's, summoned me. I went to the room and from behind the curtain which is in front of the bed I heard the Lady Princess crying out and weeping and sobbing, saying many things, among which the following: "How false were the reports which have put my daughter and myself in prison till our deaths! I never offended my King and Lord. God in heaven help us, for You will come to our aid. Daughter, pray to God that He does not fail, for He never failed anyone. Give witness Torrontero, that we have been shut in a dark prison with neither enough air nor light to be able to live; it is not possible that His Majesty should either wish it so, or permit it to be so, if he knows about it, being such a great Christian. Write to my children that they should beg His Majesty that Doctor Balleo who knows these rooms and has been in them should give account of how they could not be lived in without the grilles and of how much less now that they have become a sad, dark, death cell." '

The scribe's account continues in much the same way right through to Ana's death. Every day she presented new complaints, he recorded them, then Don Alonso's explanations, denials or justifications, and the whole lot was sent off regularly to the King. There's no doubt he received them; but he gave no instructions to Don Alonso to moderate the severity of the imprisonment. Two of the maids – Gregoria de Morales and María La Calsa – fell ill through lack of air and light and received the Last Sacraments.

Ana herself was bed-ridden and paralysed by the beginning of the winter and for days on end would not witness Mass or speak to the scribe; this continued through the whole of 1591. One recalls, and wonders if Ana did too, Teresa's vision of Hell, in that Autobiography that Ana once capriciously made fun of and sent to the Inquisition: 'At the end there was a hollow place, scooped out of a wall, like a cupboard and it was here that I found myself in close confinement . . . And even these are nothing by comparison with the agony of my soul, an oppression, a suffocation, and an affliction so deeply felt and accompanied by such hopeless and distressing misery that I cannot find words to describe it. In that pestilential spot, where I was quite powerless to hope for comfort, it was impossible to sit or lie for there was no room to do so. The very walls, so terrible to the sight, bore down upon me . . .'

Yet although the conditions in which these last months were dragged out might have daunted all but the most penitent of nuns, Ana's attitude remained intransigent. In November 1591 she wrote to her son Diego de Francavila: 'As for begging for justice as if I was guilty or delinquent, this I have never done, because I shall never recognise any guilt on my part.'

On 20 November she received the Sacraments from Don Miguel Huerta, a canon of the Collegiate Church of Pastrana. On 18 January 1592 a Doctor Simal found her still excitedly angry against Don Alonso. A fortnight later she made her will, only a few hours before she died.

It is a long document leaving an over-riding impression of a mind clear, business-like, and determined – knowing what it wants and seeking to be sure its will is done. Yet there is a dignity, a sureness of touch, a refusal to dwell histrionically or with self-pity on the approach of death or on the misery of her condition, which are truly remarkable. It shows she died a lady in spirit if a nun in physical circumstances and that, one imagines, is an epitaph she would have been satisfied with.

'I, doña Ana de Mendoza y la Cerda, Princess of Eboli, Duchess of Pastrana, widowed wife of Ruy Gómez, my Lord and Husband who abides in God, being ill in bed with the illness Our Lord saw fit to serve upon me, being in sound mind, judgment and understanding – I know what I see and understand what is said to me – fearing death which is natural but uncertain the hour of its coming; having sought to cleanse my conscience as well as human weakness and frailty will allow me or as far as I have been able to understand, I do confess and believe all that the Holy Mother Church requires I should confess, and, as a Catholic and faithful Christian, though a sinner, wishing to dispose of the worldly goods which God has seen fit to bestow upon me as has His blessed Mother the most glorious virgin Holy Mary whom I have always held as my intercessor and mediator and whom I beg to recommend me to the glory of her most precious Son so that without examining my faults and sins there should be pity and misericord upon my soul, I set out and record my last and final will in the following manner:

'Firstly I offer my soul to Our Lord God who created it and redeemed it with his most precious blood and order my body to be interred in Our Lady of the Pillar in this town of

Pastrana or in the collegiate church of the town of which I am patroness . . .

'Item: I order my body to be clothed in the habit of St. Francis* . . .'

There now followed detailed instructions regarding her funeral and the Masses to be said for her. The will then lists gifts for her servants.

'Item: I order my servant La Calsa, native of San Torcaz, to be given 1,000 ducats to help her marriage . . .

'Item: 1,000 ducats to Doña Gregoria de Morales . . . the said sum to remain in the hands of Ruy Gómez, my son, until she should marry . . .

'Item: I give to Mari Gómez another thousand ducats and order she should receive the benefits and wages of a servant of mine throughout the remaining years of her life . . .

Clearly Mari Gómez was the favourite – it has been said that she was lively, chatted to the guards, played the guitar. Diego Sánchez, her pastry cook, was also to be paid for the rest of his life – 'this is what I order for he has served me many years, and this is my will.'

Camilo Janizi, he whom Samaniego feared would turn bully-boy, clearly ended on the wrong side of the Princess, yet she treats him with scrupulous fairness: 'I order that the accounts of Camilo Janizi be examined from the time he served me as Major-Domo according to my will, and if money is due to him from that time may he be paid provided these accounts are correct; but from the time he served against my will, from then until now, may he not be paid.'

Another hint of the difficult times that were nearly over comes next.

'Item: I order that my servant Francisco Martínez from near this town be paid the wages and expenses of provisioner for all the time he has served me and may serve me, for I have not sent him out of my house.'

* This is traditional following the belief that St. Francis comes to Purgatory every three years and takes out all Franciscans and Poor Clares.

Further dispositions are made to ensure that all her local debts to servants and tradesmen are promptly paid. Ana's irresponsibilities were on a national, even an international scale; in her household, to her servants, she was everything a mistress should be, and was rewarded for the most part with their devotion.

Now comes the only direct reference to the sufferings of eleven years; it is made with a restraint that adds dignity and sharpens the irony.

'Item: I declare and state that for some time I have not enjoyed the free use of the funds and estates of the said Prince my Lord and myself, with respect to which I beg His Majesty the King, Our Lord, to see fit to order that this be looked into and that such accounts as have accumulated together with the sum left at the time I ceased to enjoy the use of it should go to the said Ruy Gómez de Silva y Mendoza, my son . . .'

After this the rest of the will is taken up with very precise instructions concerning a most sumptuous church to be raised 'to the glory of God' at Pastrana, to be served by a brotherhood of twenty 'created like the Order of Commendadores at Lisbon' whose salaries she precisely fixed at 20,000 maravedis a year, and whose duties, dress and so on were precisely laid down, and whose members should be 'clean or old Christians of neither Jewish nor Moorish race'. The church once raised should contain 'the body of Prince Ruy Gómez, my Lord, and the bodies of the Prince and Princess my worthy parents, may they be in Glory, and my body, and the bodies of all my descendants'.

Her children, Ruy Gómez Duke of Pastrana, María Duchess of Medina Sidonia, Diego Duke of Francavila, Ana de Mendoza, and the others are left equal shares in what remains, and the Dukes of Pastrana, Francavila, and Medina Sidonia are named as executors.

The will concludes with these words: 'I sign it with my

name before the scribe present. And I, the scribe, bear witness that I know her Ladyship who signs.

'The Princess doña Ana

'This happened before me: Gerónimo Torrontero.'

It was dated 2 February, 1592. The Princess died the same day.

One of her younger sons, Fray Pedro González de Mendoza – whom the will charges with seeing that the Masses are said for her soul, and who was later Archbishop of Granada and Zaragoza – undertook the enlargement of the Collegiate Church of Pastrana, and built a crypt where his parents' bodies now lie in magnificent marble tombs carved in classical style like urns. Doña Ana, the daughter who shared her imprisonment, was married after Ana's death but not long after took the veil as a Poor Clare.

Her elder sister's union with the Duke of Medina Sidonia was blessed with children amongst whom was a daughter – Luisa de Guzmán. As a child Luisa was married to John, the then Duke of Braganza. Like her Grandmother Luisa was ambitious and energetic. Like her Grandmother she had a confidential adviser – a Portuguese named João Pinto Ribeiro. In 1640 through the efforts of this pair and after a short and bloody revolution against Philip's grandson, Philip IV, the indolent Duke became John IV of Portugal and Luisa de Guzmán was crowned as his Queen. Their daughter Catherine, Ana's great-granddaughter, was also a Queen – she married Charles II of England, and later in life also ruled in Portugal as Regent. The line continued as rulers of Portugal and Brazil into the twentieth century.

'It is a wearisome thing for lords to be always lords . . . because it angers me they should be always lords and never kings.'